Contents

Answers to Revision Questions are online:

www.hodderplus.co.uk/cceagcsescience

Introduction

The purpose of this revision guide is to help students who are taking GCSE Biology or the Biology component of Double Award Science fulfil their potential in the course.

The book outlines key biological facts and explains the underlying concepts in an approachable style. Particular attention is paid to topics and types of questions that have traditionally caused most difficulty.

As well as helping with knowledge and understanding, the guide gives useful guidance in examination technique in the form of Exam tips. Many of the tips highlight common misconceptions and mistakes made by students during examinations. They also explain how to use the correct terms and critical words to maximise your marks.

Using a carefully planned revision strategy which incorporates the reinforcement of core knowledge and essential understanding, this book will enable you to achieve your very best, whether you are striving to obtain an A or A* grade, or whether you are hoping to achieve a grade C.

Format of the Guide

The chapters in this book are arranged in a similar order to its companion text, *GCSE Biology for CCEA (Second Edition)*.

In each chapter the most important points in each topic are explained and understanding is built up through the use of questions and typical answers. At the end of each chapter there are revision questions (without answers) which can be used for testing knowledge and understanding. The answers to these questions can be found on the website www.hodderplus.co.uk/cceagcsescience

Material required for the higher tier students following either the GCSE Double Award Science or the GCSE Biology specification is identified with a green tinted background.

Material required for foundation tier students following the GCSE Biology specification is identified with a blue tinted background.

Material required for higher tier students following the GCSE Biology specification is identified with a red tinted background.

Material with a yellow tint on page 41 is for Double Award Science only and not required for GCSE Biology.

Some helpful hints

Before we have a look at some of the course content it is worth noting that many students fail to maximise their performance because of misreading questions or not focusing their answers sufficiently in terms of the question. Remember examiners can only mark what they see in the paper in front of them, not what they think you meant to write!

The following words are often used in examination papers and it is important that you know exactly what each of them means. The words are often called 'command' words – they tell you what to do.

'Command' word	What you need to do
Give / name / state	Write down a short answer – possibly only one word – no explanation is needed
Complete	Answer in the spaces that have been provided – sometimes in boxes on diagrams or on answer lines at the end of the question or in gaps in a written paragraph
List	Write a series of short answers – the word 'list' suggests there is more than one possible answer
Describe	Give a detailed account
Explain	Include an explanation of *why* or *how*
Compare	Describe the similarities and/or differences in the information
Use the information in the diagram / paragraph etc.	You must use the information provided in the question in your answer
Suggest / predict	Although you will not be expected to know the answer, you should be able to deduce or estimate it, either from information provided or from your knowledge

Sometimes two or more of these terms can be used together in one question. For example, many questions start with 'Describe and explain ....'. These questions are almost always worth at least two marks: 1 mark for describing and at least 1 for the explanation.

It is also important to recognise that if a question is worth 3 marks then you will usually need to make three separate points in your answer to gain full marks.

Many students may think that the comments above simply state the obvious. However, it is amazing how many candidates are caught out by not following these rules.

What are assessment objectives?

Assessment objectives (AOs) summarise the knowledge and skills candidates are expected to develop as they follow a GCSE course. There are three assessment objectives outlining different categories of skills. The DAS and GCSE Biology assessment objectives are listed in the following table.

AO1	Recall, select and communicate their knowledge and understanding of biology
AO2	Apply skills, knowledge and understanding of biology in practical and other contexts
AO3	Analyse and evaluate evidence, make reasoned judgements and draw conclusions based on evidence

The assessment objectives are important in that each examination paper must test each of AO1, AO2 and AO3. You will only be able to answer AO1 questions if you know and understand the biological content in the specification. AO2 questions involve the application of skills. These skills include the drawing of graphs, carrying out calculations and applying your knowledge in unfamiliar situations. AO3 questions often involve the presentation of results from an experiment, or a set of data and ask you to analyse the evidence and make considered judgements on the evidence provided.

To develop good examination technique in answering AO2 and AO3 questions in particular, it is important that you reinforce your knowledge and skills by practising on examination questions. Good examples can be found in this book, in the companion text *GCSE Biology for CCEA (Second Edition)*, or from past examination papers.

Note: *AO2 and AO3 are also tested in the* **Controlled Assessment Task**.

The QWC questions

Most of the question parts in each examination range from 1–3 marks. However, there will be Quality of Written Communication (QWC) questions worth 6 marks. While these questions will be testing your ability to communicate biological information in a logical way using appropriate scientific terminology, you can only access the full range of marks available if you understand and describe the biology involved.

www.ccea.org.uk is the site to use when requiring further information about the **specification** and assessment objectives, **past papers** and **Chief Examiners' reports**. The Chief Examiners' reports provide information for teachers and candidates on candidate performance in each series of examinations.

1 Cells

This table summarises the major components of the three types of cell and their functions.

Structure	Function	Cell type		
		Animal	Plant	Bacterial
Cell membrane	Controls entry and exit of substances – **selectively permeable**	✓	✓	✓
Cell wall	Rigid structure providing structural integrity – **fully permeable**	–	✓ (cellulose)	✓ (non - cellulose)
Cytoplasm	Site of **chemical reactions**, jelly-like fluid	✓	✓	✓
Nucleus	Contains genetic information in the form of **chromosomes**	✓	✓	–
Nuclear membrane	Surrounds **nucleus**	✓	✓	–
Chloroplast	Site of photosynthesis, contains **chlorophyll**	–	✓	–
Permanent vacuole	Storage of salts and sugars and provides **turgor**	–	✓	–

Exam tip

Plant and animal cells are much larger than bacterial cells.

Plant cells tend to have a regular shape because of their cell walls.

Bacterial cells contain a large loop of DNA in addition to many small rings of DNA called **plasmids**.

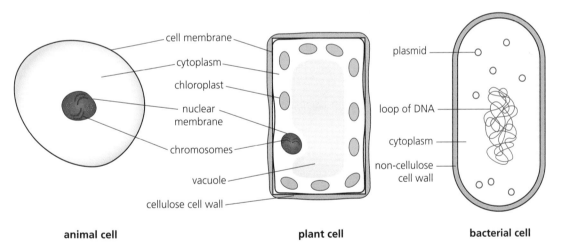

animal cell   plant cell   bacterial cell

↑ **Figure 1.1 The structure of animal, plant and bacterial cells**

Magnification is the number of times larger the image appears when compared to the object. The following equations can often be helpful when calculating magnifications or the actual size of a specimen.

$$\text{actual size} = \frac{\text{observed size}}{\text{magnification}}$$

$$\text{magnification} = \frac{\text{observed size}}{\text{actual size}}$$

Pictures produced from microscopes (micrographs) can also have a scale bar drawn on them. In these cases the image is much bigger than the actual object.

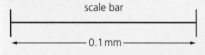

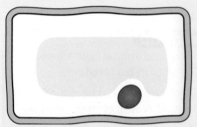

↑ **Figure 1.2 Whole cell with scale bar and its representative length**

Worked example

Ruth has been provided with a photograph of a cell with a scale bar. The scale bar is shown here.

←————————→
0.1 mm

Using the information provided, calculate the magnification used to produce the photograph. **[3 marks]**

Answer

Measurement of the scale bar (using a ruler) = 5 cm

Convert to mm = 50 mm

$$\frac{50\,\text{mm}}{0.1\,\text{mm}} = \times\,500$$

Remember to ensure that you put '✕' in front of any magnification.

Levels of organisation

Revised

As organisms increase in size, they have more difficulty exchanging and transporting substances between their cells, as well as communicating between the cells. To improve the efficiency of exchange, transport and communication processes, multicellular organisms have evolved various levels of organisation.

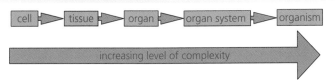

↑ **Figure 1.3 Flow diagram to show the levels of organisation in multicellular organisms**

Growth and development

Revised

Although plants and animals share the levels of organisation described in Figure 1.3, they have very different patterns of growth.

Animal growth tends to involve growth all over their bodies whereas plants tend to grow only at the tips of their roots and shoots (the **apices**).

The reason for this is that only certain areas of the plant have the ability to grow. These areas are called **meristems**. Meristematic tissues are made up of unspecialised cells that have the ability to become any type of plant cell. Plants have these cells for the duration of their life. This is why gardeners can take cuttings (a selected section cut from a plant) and grow whole new plants from the cutting.

In animals, cells become specialised at an early stage of development. All specialised cells differentiate from stem cells. **Stem cells** can grow into any type of body cell and are therefore of interest in developing new treatments for diseases.

Ethical implications of stem cell research

There are three major sources of stem cells:

● umbilical cord blood

● embryos

● adult cells.

Some groups believe that the types of procedures used to harvest stem cells are controversial as life can be created artificially. Others have concerns that people seek to have so-called 'designer babies', for example in order to provide stem cells for the treatment of illnesses in other family members.

The use of stem cells is now being investigated as a way of producing meat in a cheaper and more efficient way. It is possible to grow muscle tissue from a cow, pig or chicken which could then be used as a food source. It is hoped that this would be cheaper as the costs of feeding and keeping animals would be greatly reduced.

> **Exam tip**
>
> It is important to recognise that questions involving consideration of ethical implications require a balanced answer, so you need to take into account the positives and negatives of the matter in the question. In the area of stem cell research, it may be the case that the technology allows lives to be saved – but does this warrant the use of human embryos in order to develop a cure? You may need to take account of both sides when answering.

Diffusion

Diffusion is the process responsible for the movement of many substances into and out of cells. It is defined as follows:

'Diffusion is the random molecular movement of molecules from a region of high concentration to a region of lower concentration along a concentration gradient.'

The process can be easily demonstrated using dye crystals in a beaker of water. The colour of the dye is eventually distributed evenly throughout the water as the dye crystals spread out from their initial concentration in one place. Another common demonstration makes use of a sugar solution in visking tubing immersed in a beaker of water.

Diffusion is an important process as it allows exchange of substances, for example gas exchange in the lungs and in the leaves of plants.

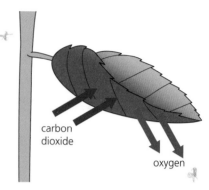

carbon
dioxide

oxygen

↑ **Figure 1.4** Diffusion is important in the movement of gases into and out of leaves as shown in photosynthesis

Revision Questions

1 Sort the following into order from the most simple to the most complex:

stomach; digestive system; muscle cell; stomach wall muscle tissue; rat   **[1 mark]**

2 Match the following cell structures with their functions:

cell membrane	carries out photosynthesis
chloroplast	the site of chemical reactions
cytoplasm	controls entry and exit of substances

[2 marks]

3 Copy and complete the following table by placing a tick if present or a cross if absent in the different types of cells.

Structure	Plant cell	Bacterial cell
Cell membrane	✓	✓
Circular chromosome		✓
Chloroplast	✓	
Cytoplasm	✓	✓
Cellulose cell wall	✓	
Nuclear membrane	✓	

[3 marks]

4 Place the following statements about using a microscope in the correct order – use only the letters:

B, E, A D C

A) focus by turning the coarse focus knob to move the stage down away from the objective lens

B) ensure the low power objective lens is in position and the stage is in its lowest position

C) ensure that the stage is fully lowered before removing the slide

D) without looking down the eyepiece, move the stage as close to the lens as possible without it touching the slide

E) place the slide on the stage   **[3 marks]**

Go online for the answers

Online

2 Photosynthesis and Plants

Look at the equations below.

$$\text{carbon dioxide} + \text{water} \xrightarrow[\text{light}]{\text{chlorophyll}} \text{glucose} + \text{oxygen}$$

$$6CO_2 + 6H_2O \xrightarrow[\text{light}]{\text{chlorophyll}} C_6H_{12}O_6 + 6O_2$$

These equations summarise the process of **photosynthesis** and can be derived or proven through investigations into photosynthesis.

Investigating photosynthesis   Revised ☐

A key aspect of many of these investigations is testing leaves for starch. Leaves convert the glucose made during photosynthesis into starch for storage, so this test indicates that photosynthesis has taken place. In order to make the experiment a fair test, first leaves must be **destarched** (by placing the plant in darkness for 48 hours) before the plant is exposed to the experimental conditions. This makes sure that any starch detected has been produced during the experiment and was not present before.

The table summarises the reason for each stage in the process of testing a leaf for starch.

Stage	Process	Reason
1	Boiling the leaf in water	Stops reactions in the leaf Removes waxy cuticle
2	Boiling the leaf in ethanol	Removes chlorophyll to allow iodine colour to be judged more easily
3	Leaf dipped into hot water	Softens the leaf (as ethanol makes it brittle)
4	Iodine added	A colour change from yellow–brown to blue–black indicates the presence of starch and therefore that photosynthesis has occurred

Exam tip

Make sure that if you are asked to give a colour change you state the start colour and end colour.
For example:
Q. What is the colour change for a positive starch test?
A. Iodine changes *from* yellow–brown *to* blue–black.

Photosynthesis experiments

Using the starch test described on page II, different experiments can be done to show that chlorophyll, carbon dioxide and light are all necessary for photosynthesis to take place. The table gives details of the experiments.

Experiment	To show chlorophyll is necessary	To show carbon dioxide is necessary	To show light is necessary
Method	Use of previously destarched **variegated** leaves (leaves with white areas that lack chlorophyll). Plant left in bright light for two days.	Remove carbon dioxide from the air around a previously destarched plant using sodium hydroxide. A second leaf or plant should be set up as a control.	Partially covering a leaf from a previously destarched plant with black paper or tinfoil.
	white edge lacking chlorophyll green central area containing chlorophyll	clear plastic bag sodium hydroxide solution — elastic band	black paper or tinfoil
Expected result of starch test	The original white areas of the leaf should produce a negative result (yellow–brown), the original green areas should produce a positive result (blue–black).	Leaves exposed to air with carbon dioxide removed should produce a negative result.	Areas of leaf that are exposed to light produce a positive result (iodine turns blue–black). Covered areas produce a negative result (iodine remains yellow–brown).
Explanation	Chlorophyll is needed to absorb light. Areas without it cannot photosynthesise.	Carbon dioxide is a reactant. If it is absent the water has nothing to react with so no photosynthesis can occur.	Light is the form of energy required to drive photosynthesis. If light is blocked the leaf cannot photosynthesise so no starch is produced.

A water plant such as Canadian pondweed (*Elodea*) can be used to prove that oxygen is made during photosynthesis. It can be shown that the gas collected is oxygen by using the glowing splint test (oxygen relights a glowing splint).

The apparatus can also be used to estimate the rate of photosynthesis under different conditions by counting the number of (oxygen) bubbles released per unit time from a freshly cut section of *Elodea*.

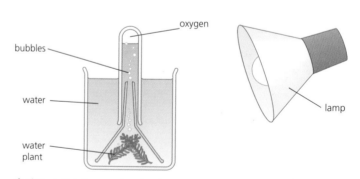

↑ **Figure 2.1 Apparatus to demonstrate oxygen production**

The conditions in which the *Elodea* is kept can be altered in order to investigate the effects of different factors on the rate of photosynthesis, for example light intensity can be altered by placing the lamp in Figure 2.1 at different distances from the beaker.

How leaf structure is adapted for photosynthesis

Leaves have adaptations to make the process of photosynthesis more efficient.

upper side of leaf

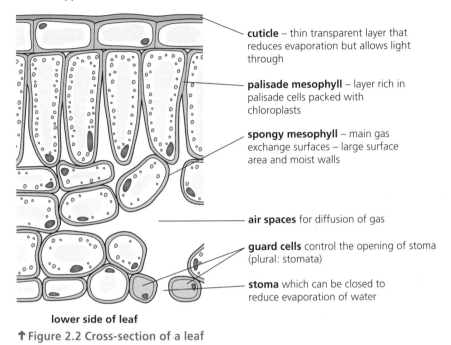

cuticle – thin transparent layer that reduces evaporation but allows light through

palisade mesophyll – layer rich in palisade cells packed with chloroplasts

spongy mesophyll – main gas exchange surfaces – large surface area and moist walls

air spaces for diffusion of gas

guard cells control the opening of stoma (plural: stomata)

stoma which can be closed to reduce evaporation of water

lower side of leaf

↑ Figure 2.2 Cross-section of a leaf

Photosynthesis is made more efficient by:

Light absorption

Leaves are broad and flat to create a large surface area over which light can be absorbed.

The **palisade mesophyll** layer is composed of tall thin cells crammed full of chlorophyll-containing chloroplasts to absorb light energy.

The waxy **cuticle** is transparent to allow light to enter.

Gas exchange

The **spongy mesophyll** layer has many intercellular spaces (gaps between cells) to allow gases to move easily from the place where they enter the leaf to the palisade layer.

The epidermis of the leaf is perforated by many stomata, which are pores through which the carbon dioxide needed for photosynthesis can enter the leaf.

Guard cells surrounding each stoma can change shape in order to control the size of the pore.

> **Exam tip**
>
> Remember that most land plants have a higher density of stomata on the underside of the leaf; water dwelling plants such as water lilies tend to have more on the upper surface.

Photosynthesis and respiration

Revised

Photosynthesis and respiration are closely linked. The products of photosynthesis (glucose and oxygen) are used for respiration and the carbon dioxide and water released from respiration can be used for photosynthesis.

We have seen that light is required for photosynthesis to occur – it therefore only happens during daylight hours in plants. Respiration is a process that occurs at all times in all living organisms.

The level of carbon dioxide is a good indicator of the relative balance between the two processes. This is easily detected by the colour changes of hydrogencarbonate indicator outlined in the diagram.

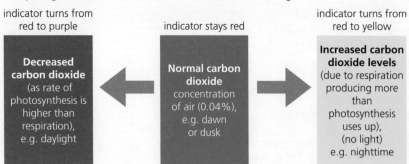

↑ Figure 2.3 Colour changes of hydrogencarbonate indicator

Low light intensities at times such as dawn and dusk often result in the rate of photosynthesis and respiration being equal. At this point there is no exchange of carbon dioxide as the amount needed by photosynthesis is exactly matched by the amount released from respiration (shown by the middle box in Figure 2.3).

This is called the **compensation point**.

Using the products of photosynthesis

Revised

The uses of the products of photosynthesis fall into three categories as shown in the table.

How product is used	Details	Notes
Growth	Glucose can be converted into amino acids that make up proteins and also into cellulose which is needed for new cell walls	Minerals are needed for glucose to be converted into other molecules
Storage	Much of the glucose produced is converted to starch and stored	Many plants have large stores of starch located in one region, e.g. potatoes and turnips store starch in their roots
Respiration	Oxygen and glucose are needed for respiration	Glucose can also be converted into lipids (oils) that can be used in respiration

A further use not described in the table is reproduction. Nectar, which is present in some flowers attracts insects which then go on to spread pollen from the flowers, is produced from glucose.

Worked example

A group of students was asked to study two leaves and use a simple method to count the number of stomata per unit area (stomatal density) on the upper and lower surfaces of the leaves. Their results are shown here.

Leaf 1, upper surface: 25 stomata per square centimetre

Leaf 2, upper surface: 100 stomata per square centimetre

Leaf 1, lower surface: 75 stomata per square centimetre

Leaf 2, lower surface: 30 stomata per square centimetre

a) Present these results in a suitable table. [3 marks]

b) Each group only used one leaf of each type. How could the class have made its results more reliable? [1 mark]

Answer

a) The data can be arranged in columns or rows. Ensure that column / row headings include units where appropriate (number of stomata /cm^2) and that data are clear for both leaf 1 and leaf 2:

Leaf	Number of stomata / cm^2	
	Upper surface	**Lower surface**
1	25	75
2	100	30

b) Your answer here must reflect a clear understanding of reliability in experiments. This is most often achieved by repeating experiments, but in this case the class results could be collated and used to obtain average values.

Limiting factors and economic implications

Revised ☐

Look at the graph of how the rate of photosynthesis varies with light intensity.

The factor that is in shortest supply is referred to as the **limiting factor**.

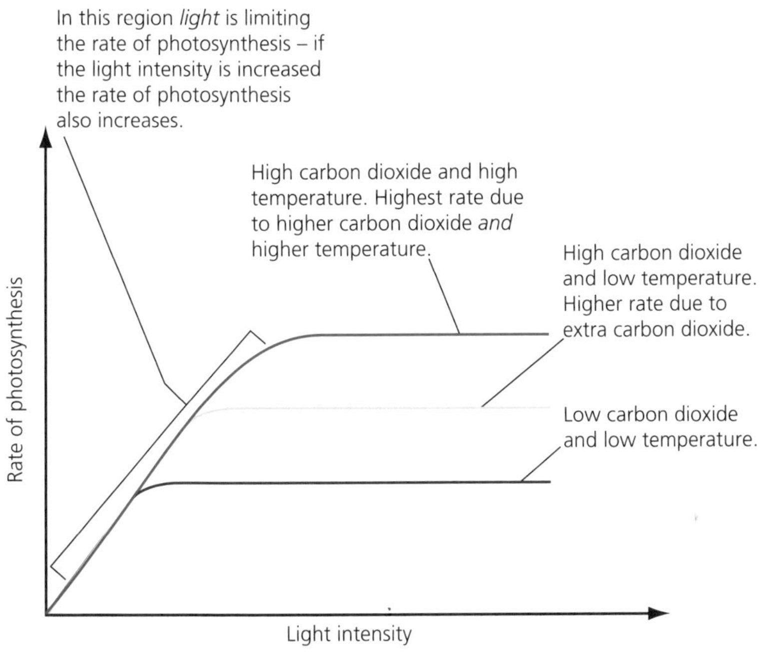

In this region *light* is limiting the rate of photosynthesis – if the light intensity is increased the rate of photosynthesis also increases.

High carbon dioxide and high temperature. Highest rate due to higher carbon dioxide *and* higher temperature.

High carbon dioxide and low temperature. Higher rate due to extra carbon dioxide.

Low carbon dioxide and low temperature.

Rate of photosynthesis

Light intensity

↑ **Figure 2.4 Graphical explanation of limiting factors**

Growers of crops such as tomatoes and cucumbers often install equipment in their glasshouses to boost the growth of their plants and therefore the amount of crop produced (called the **yield**).

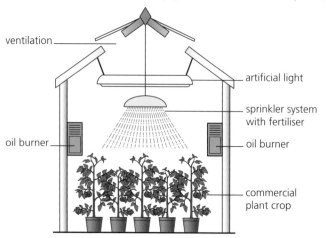

⬆ **Figure 2.5 Strategies to improve photosynthesis and growth**

3 Nutrition and Health

Energy requirements and health Revised

The amount of energy you need depends on three key factors:

- age
- gender
- level of activity.

In addition to this, during pregnancy, expectant mothers require more energy to allow the development of their foetus.

In order to determine how much energy a person requires, the **Harris Benedict** model can be used to calculate the **Basal Metabolic Rate (BMR)** – the amount of energy required to maintain a constant body mass at rest. This model takes into account your activity levels, size, age and gender.

If a person's diet provides more energy than they use during normal day-to-day activities then they will store any excess as fat. Over time this can lead to obesity. Health professionals often use a person's **body mass index (BMI)** along with blood pressure readings to assess their general health. To calculate BMI divide the person's weight (kg) by the square of their height (m).

In order to maintain a healthy body it is recommended that all diets should contain plenty of fresh fruit and vegetables and keep the amounts of salty, sugary and fatty foods to a minimum. This is reflected by government health initiatives such as the **'5 a day' campaign**. In consuming a healthy diet individuals stand a better chance of avoiding conditions such as obesity, stroke, heart disease, diabetes, arthritis and high blood pressure.

> **Exam tip**
>
> Make sure that you can explain the need for the government to take action over the current high levels of obesity.
>
> For example, higher levels of diet-related illnesses need more treatment and this is putting more pressure on the National Health Service and is costing the country more. This may result in increased taxation.

Energy in food

The energy content of a given food can be calculated by using the following equation:

energy released / J = mass of water / g × rise in temperature / °C × 4.2

In order to obtain data to use in the equation different foods can be burned under a known mass of water. The temperature of the water can be recorded before and after the experiment in order to calculate temperature change. Figure 3.1 shows how this can be carried out in the laboratory.

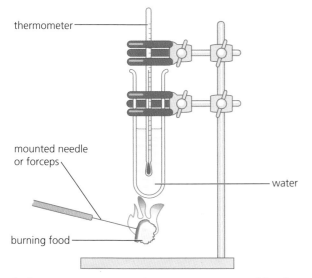

thermometer

mounted needle or forceps

water

burning food

↑ **Figure 3.1 Measuring the energy content of food**

Investigating food samples using food tests

Human diets contain a range of food groups. The table summarises the food tests that can be used to determine the food groups present in a given food.

Food group		Name of test	Method	Positive result
Carbohydrates	Sugar	Benedict's	Add equal volume of Benedict's solution; heat carefully in a water bath	Solution changes from **blue** to **brick red** colour (green or orange indicates small amounts of sugar)
	Starch	Iodine	Add iodine	Iodine changes from **yellow–brown** to **blue–black**
Protein		Biuret	Add sodium hydroxide followed by a few drops of copper sulfate; shake	Solution changes from a light **blue** to **purple** / mauve or lilac colour
Fats and oils		Emulsion (ethanol)	Extract oils / fats in ethanol; add to an equal volume of cold water	On contact with water solution forms a **white** emulsion
Vitamin C		DCPIP	Add drops of the food juice to DCPIP	DCPIP changes from **blue** to pink and then becomes **colourless**

Balanced diet

A balanced diet is one that contributes the correct levels of each of the food groups: carbohydrates, proteins, fats, vitamins, minerals, water and fibre. If a diet contains too much or too little of any of these groups the person will become malnourished.

Food groups

The table summarises the food groups.

Food group		Why needed	Good sources	Notes / deficiency problems
Carbohydrates	Glucose	Provides energy rapidly	Sweets, chocolate etc.	Carbohydrates provide 17 kJ/g. All carbohydrates are composed of carbon, hydrogen and oxygen
	Lactose	Provides energy rapidly	Milk (including breast milk)	
	Cellulose	Indigestible – the bulk of fibre is composed of cellulose	All plant material (plant cell walls are composed of cellulose)	
	Starch	Slow release energy	Bread, rice, potatoes, pasta	Composed of chains of glucose
	Glycogen	Energy storage in animal cells	All animal material especially red meat	Most animals store a lot of glycogen in muscles and liver
Proteins		Growth and repair	Meat, fish, eggs, peas and beans	Composed of carbon, hydrogen, oxygen and nitrogen, provide 18 kJ/g
Fats		Energy, insulation	Butter, fried food	Composed of carbon, hydrogen, oxygen, provide 38 kJ/g

Food group		Why needed	Good sources	Notes / deficiency problems
Vitamins	C	Maintains cell health, especially the cells found in the walls of blood vessels	Citrus fruits (oranges, lemons and limes), blackcurrants	A lack of vitamin C leads to scurvy – gums deteriorate and teeth can be lost
	D	For strong bones and teeth	Found in fish oils, liver, eggs, milk and is made by the pigments in the skin when exposed to sunlight	A lack of vitamin D leads to rickets – bones soften and can often bow under body weight
Minerals	Iron	Part of the haemoglobin molecule in red blood cells needed to transport oxygen	Red meat, liver, green vegetables	Anaemia – due to a lack of red blood cells, lack of energy due to poor oxygen supply
	Calcium	Needed for strong bones and teeth, muscle contraction and blood clotting	Milk, cheese, vegetables	A lack of calcium can lead to osteoporosis (brittle bones) in later life
Water		All reactions take place in solution, transport (blood plasma), fluid in joints, cytoplasm in cells	All drinks, fresh fruit and vegetables	Dehydration can lead to loss of cell function
Fibre		Essential to prevent constipation and maintain a healthy digestive system	Wholemeal bread, fresh fruit and vegetables, cereals	Most fibre is the cellulose found in plant cell walls

Worked example

Copy and complete the following table.

Food group	Use in the body	Source
Starch	a)	Rice
b)	Energy and insulation	c)
d)	e)	Chicken

[5 marks]

Answer

a) Energy.

b) Fat.

c) Butter.

d) Protein.

e) Growth and repair.

Exam tip

In your answers to **a)** starchy foods such as rice are the element of the diet that are most often associated with energy provision; **b)** make sure in questions such as these you give answers that cannot be deemed as vague (e.g. some fish do provide plenty of oil but not all fish do) and **c)** make sure you give growth and repair, leave nothing to chance in exams as it could be worth 2 marks – 1 for growth and 1 for repair.

1 A student has been asked to carry out tests on a solution containing a number of different food groups. The results are as follows:

- Benedict's solution turns brick red
- iodine remained yellow–brown
- Biuret solution turned from blue to purple
- DCPIP changed from blue to colourless.

What food groups are present in the test solution? [3 marks]

2 What are the main functions of the following food groups in the diet:

a) proteins

b) fats

c) fibre? [3 marks]

3 The tables show some of the nutrients found in two brands of crisps.

Brand A	
Nutrient	**Amount / g per 100 g**
Protein	6.0
Fat	8.1
Carbohydrate (of which sugars)	73.5 7.0
Fibre	4.6

Brand B	
Nutrient	**Amount / g per 100 g**
Protein	5.5
Fat	33.0
Carbohydrate (of which sugars)	56.0 8.5
Fibre	1.2

a) Both brands of crisps are sold as 'healthier options'. Which brand's claims are more accurate? Explain your answer. [3 marks]

b) The guideline daily amount (GDA) of fat for an adult male is 95 g. If a man ate 100 g of brand A crisps what percentage of his GDA for fat would he receive? Show your working. [2 marks]

4 It is possible to determine the amount of energy in a food experimentally by burning 1g of food under a test tube containing a known volume of water. The temperature increase of the water can be recorded using a thermometer and the energy content calculated by applying the following equation:

Amount of energy in food / J = temperature rise / $^{\circ}$C × volume of water cm^3 × 4.2

The table below indicates data collected by a group of students. They used 20 cm^3 of water in each experiment.

Food	Initial temperature / $^{\circ}$C	Final temperature / $^{\circ}$C	Temperature change / $^{\circ}$C	Energy in food / kJ
Peanut	21	78		
Potato crisp	22	64		
Pasta	20	58		

a) Calculate the temperature change and insert these into the relevant column in the table. [3 marks]

b) Use the formula provided to calculate the energy in each food in kJ. [4 marks]

Go online for the answers — Online

4 Digestion and Enzymes

Details of digestion

The process of digestion takes place along the length of the digestive system, sometimes referred to as the alimentary canal or digestive tract.

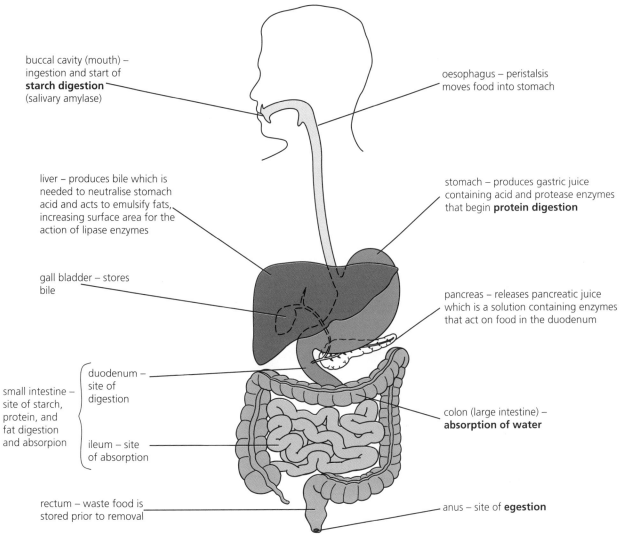

buccal cavity (mouth) – ingestion and start of **starch digestion** (salivary amylase)

oesophagus – peristalsis moves food into stomach

liver – produces bile which is needed to neutralise stomach acid and acts to emulsify fats, increasing surface area for the action of lipase enzymes

stomach – produces gastric juice containing acid and protease enzymes that begin **protein digestion**

gall bladder – stores bile

pancreas – releases pancreatic juice which is a solution containing enzymes that act on food in the duodenum

small intestine – site of starch, protein, and fat digestion and absorpion

duodenum – site of digestion

ileum – site of absorption

colon (large intestine) – **absorption of water**

rectum – waste food is stored prior to removal

anus – site of **egestion**

↑ **Figure 4.1 The alimentary canal and its functions**

Absorption

When food has been digested, the products of digestion must be transported around the body to the places they are needed. However they first need to be absorbed in the ileum (the lower part of the small intestine) to get into the blood supply. To facilitate this, the ileum has the following adaptations:

- a large surface area because of its long length, numerous folds and lots of villi (finger-like projections sticking out into the lumen of the gut)
- thin and permeable membranes
- a good blood supply that ensures a concentration gradient is maintained.

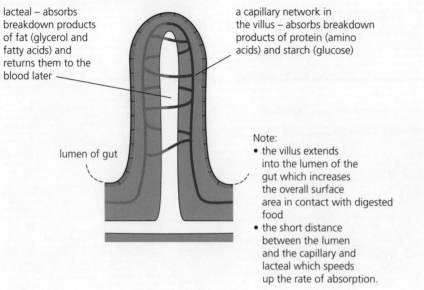

lacteal – absorbs breakdown products of fat (glycerol and fatty acids) and returns them to the blood later

a capillary network in the villus – absorbs breakdown products of protein (amino acids) and starch (glucose)

lumen of gut

Note:
- the villus extends into the lumen of the gut which increases the overall surface area in contact with digested food
- the short distance between the lumen and the capillary and lacteal which speeds up the rate of absorption.

↑ **Figure 4.2 Structure and function of a villus**

Enzymes

Enzymes are special proteins that help speed up chemical reactions. They are particularly important in the digestive system where they help break down food.

How do enzymes work?

Enzymes are biological catalysts that speed up chemical reactions (both breaking down and building up compounds).

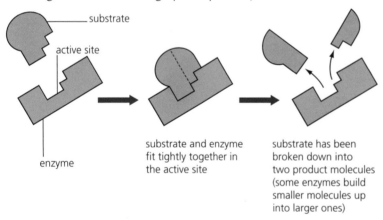

substrate

active site

enzyme

substrate and enzyme fit tightly together in the active site

substrate has been broken down into two product molecules (some enzymes build smaller molecules up into larger ones)

↑ **Figure 4.3 How enzymes work**

As you can see in Figure 4.3, the active site is complementary in shape to the substrate – they work together like a '**lock and key**'. This explains the process of **enzyme specificity**. Each enzyme fits only one substrate (or a very small number) and therefore there is a different enzyme for each reaction.

Effects of temperature, pH and enzyme concentration on enzyme action

Revised

The effects of temperature, pH and enzyme concentration on enzyme activity are shown in Figures 4.4 to 4.6.

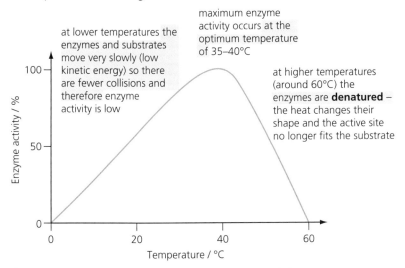

maximum enzyme activity occurs at the optimum temperature of 35–40°C
at lower temperatures the enzymes and substrates move very slowly (low kinetic energy) so there are fewer collisions and therefore enzyme activity is low
at higher temperatures (around 60°C) the enzymes are **denatured** – the heat changes their shape and the active site no longer fits the substrate
100
50
0
Enzyme activity / %
0
20
40
60
Temperature / °C

↑ **Figure 4.4 Effect of temperature on enzyme activity**

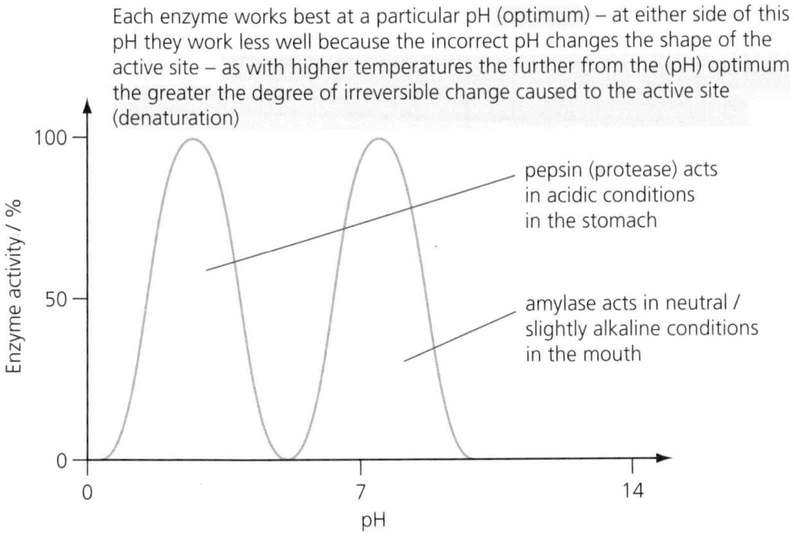

Each enzyme works best at a particular pH (optimum) – at either side of this pH they work less well because the incorrect pH changes the shape of the active site – as with higher temperatures the further from the (pH) optimum the greater the degree of irreversible change caused to the active site (denaturation)
pepsin (protease) acts in acidic conditions in the stomach
amylase acts in neutral / slightly alkaline conditions in the mouth
100
50
0
Enzyme activity / %
0
7
14
pH

↑ **Figure 4.5 Effect of pH on enzyme activity**

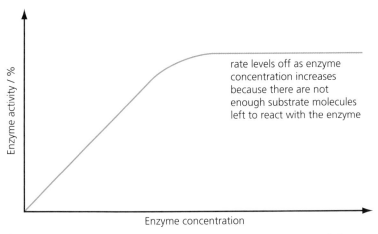

rate levels off as enzyme concentration increases because there are not enough substrate molecules left to react with the enzyme
Enzyme activity / %
Enzyme concentration

↑ **Figure 4.6 Effect of enzyme concentration on enzyme activity**

Digestive enzymes

The importance of enzymes in digestion is to break large insoluble molecules into smaller soluble molecules that can then enter the blood stream. These soluble molecules can be absorbed by all the cells in the body for use.

The table summarises the details of the enzymes involved in food digestion.

Enzyme	Food digested	Products of digestion	Where in digestive system	Sources of enzyme
Amylase	Starch	Glucose	Mouth, duodenum / small intestine	Saliva from salivary glands, pancreatic juice (from pancreas) and intestinal juice (from wall of small intestine)
Protease	Protein	Amino acids	Stomach, duodenum / small intestine	Gastric juice, pancreatic juice and intestinal juice
Lipase	Fat (lipid)	Glycerol and fatty acids	Duodenum / small intestine	Pancreatic juice and intestinal juice

Exam tip

Make sure that you can use the terms **'denatured'** and **'optimum temperature / pH'** in the correct way. Enzymes can become denatured (an irreversible process) at extremes of pH and at high temperatures. The activity of enzymes is halted when denaturation happens because the shape of the active site is no longer able to accept the substrate. The optimum temperature and pH are the values at which the enzymes function at their fastest rates. In the human body, enzymes function best at 37°C but optimum pH can vary. Some enzymes work best around pH 7 (neutral pH), but those found in the stomach have an optimum pH closer to 3 because of the acidic environment.

Enzymes have many other uses apart from digestion and many have been isolated for use in cleaning products as well as in many commercial applications. An example would be in biological washing powders where enzymes of different types are used to break down the stains on clothing.

Worked example

A group of students was investigating the effects of pH on the breakdown of protein in jelly (gelatin) by an enzyme. They cut small cubes of jelly and recorded the time taken for the jelly to dissolve. Their results are shown in the table:

pH	Time taken for jelly to dissolve / minutes
3	12
4	15
5	16
6	18
7	42
8	No effect
9	No effect

a) State what type of enzyme the students were using. [1 mark]

b) At what pH did this enzyme work best? Explain how you arrived at your answer. [2 marks]

c) Describe and explain where the enzyme being investigated may be found in the body. [2 marks]

d) Explain the results obtained at pH 8 and 9. [2 marks]

e) How could the students make their investigation more reliable? [1 mark]

Answers

a) Protease.

b) The enzyme worked best at a pH of 3.

c) The stomach.

d) Any two from: the enzyme has been denatured / damaged; by the extreme pH; the active site can no longer recognise the protein molecules in the jelly.

e) Repeat the experiment.

1 Bile is an important substance in the digestion of foods. The diagram shows one aspect of digestion related to bile:

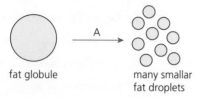

fat globule   many smallar
                           fat droplets

a) Where is bile made?   [1 mark]

b) i)   Name the process A represented by the arrow.   [1 mark]

   ii) Explain how process A aids digestion.   [2 marks]

c) Bile also plays a role in neutralising stomach acid as food moves into the duodenum. Explain why this is important if digestion is to continue in the duodenum.   [2 marks]

2 Copy the information below, then match the enzyme to the substrate it acts on in digestion.
                                                                              [2 marks]

Amylase   Fats

Pepsin (a protease)   Starch

Lipase   Protein

3 Describe three features of the small intestine that allow the absorption of digested food to happen in an efficient way.   [3 marks]

4 A group of students carried out a simple experiment to assess the effects of temperature on break down of starch by an enzyme.

a) Name the enzyme that breaks down starch.   [1 mark]

b) During the investigation what chemical test could be used to determine the presence of starch?   [1 mark]

c) The table below shows the students' results:

Temperature / °C	Time for starch digestion / seconds
25	220
35	180
45	250
55	no digestion

   i)   At which temperature did the enzyme work most efficiently? Explain how you arrived at your answer.   [2 marks]

   ii) Explain the result obtained at 55°C.   [2 marks]

5 Describe the function of each of the following organs in the digestion of food:

a) stomach   [1 mark]

b) colon / large intestine   [1 mark]

c) ileum   [1 mark]

Go online for the answers   Online

5 Breathing and the Respiratory System

The respiratory system

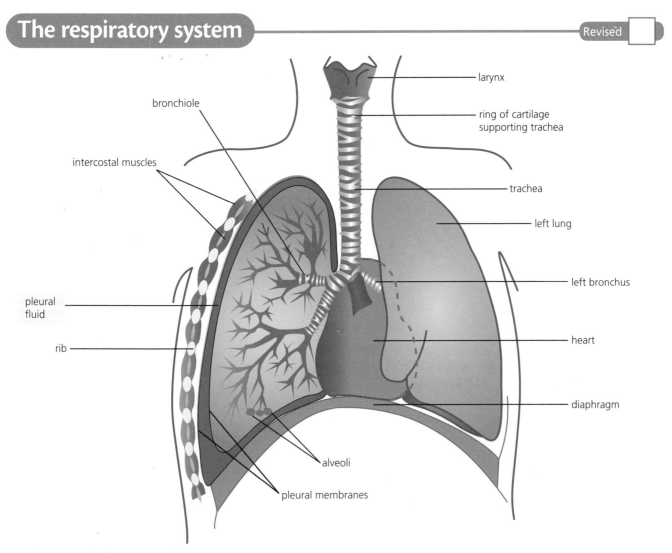

↑ **Figure 5.1 The structure of the respiratory system**

The process of breathing

Breathing is the physical process that ensures gas exchange can take place at the alveoli. At the alveoli the oxygen needed for respiration is absorbed by the blood and the waste carbon dioxide is removed from the blood. The movement of both gases occurs by diffusion and the process of breathing maintains the concentration gradients required.

The mechanism of breathing is best demonstrated by considering a model lung. The simple apparatus shown in Figure 5.2 allows the relationship between pressure and volume to be seen clearly. One breath involves a complete cycle of breathing in and breathing out.

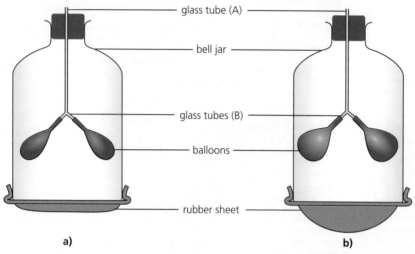

a) b)

↑ **Figure 5.2 The bell jar lung model**

Modelling inhaling (breathing in)

● With the rubber sheet (representing the diaphragm) in its raised position (Figure 5.2a), the pressure in the jar is equal to the surrounding air pressure.

● When the rubber sheet is pulled down (Figure 5.2b), the volume of the bell jar (the chest cavity) is increased.

● This results in a fall in the air pressure compared with the external air pressure.

● Air therefore rushes in via the glass tubes A and B (representing the trachea and bronchi respectively) to fill the balloons (which represent the lungs) and balance the pressure.

Modelling exhaling (breathing out)

● When the rubber sheet is released it returns to its flatter position.

● The volume in the bell jar is thus decreased.

● This means that the air pressure inside the jar is increased above the surrounding air pressure.

● Air is therefore forced out through tubes B and A and the balloons deflate.

Comparing the model lung to the respiratory system

Although the model lung demonstrates the breathing cycle in terms of volume and pressure changes very clearly, it does not show all the features and mechanisms of the human respiratory system shown in Figure 5.3. The major differences are outlined below:

1 The model lung uses a rigid walled glass bell jar but the respiratory system has a ribcage with intercostal muscles that are involved in raising and lowering the ribcage (this also acts to change volume and pressure within the chest cavity)

2 The balloons are composed of one large air space, but human lungs are composed of millions of tiny alveoli.

3 The model lung does not include any structures to represent the nasal cavity or bronchioles – only the trachea and bronchi are represented.

4 The glass tubes of the model are inflexible, unlike the trachea and bronchi. The model does not represent the C-shaped rings of cartilage that hold the trachea open either.

5 Human lungs are surrounded with a pleural membrane that contains the pleural fluid. Both of these structures are omitted from the model. These act to reduce friction between the lungs and the wall of the chest cavity during the breathing process.

> **Exam tip**
>
> A common misconception is that it is air entering the lungs that causes the diaphragm to be forced down and the ribs to be forced up and out. Make sure that you understand that it is the ribs that move up and out by the action of the intercostal muscles and the diaphragm that is pulled down by muscular contraction. The resulting increase in volume and decrease in pressure causes air to rush into the lungs, which therefore inflate.

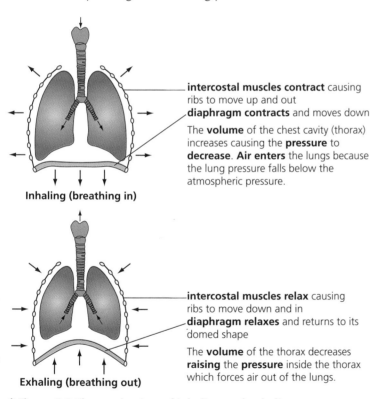

intercostal muscles contract causing ribs to move up and out
diaphragm contracts and moves down

The **volume** of the chest cavity (thorax) increases causing the **pressure** to **decrease**. **Air enters** the lungs because the lung pressure falls below the atmospheric pressure.

Inhaling (breathing in)

intercostal muscles relax causing ribs to move down and in
diaphragm relaxes and returns to its domed shape

The **volume** of the thorax decreases **raising** the **pressure** inside the thorax which forces air out of the lungs.

Exhaling (breathing out)

↑ **Figure 5.3 The mechanism of inhaling and exhaling**

The table summarises the processes of inhaling and exhaling.

Stage of breathing cycle	Details of process					
	Diaphragm	Intercostal muscles	Ribcage position	Volume	Pressure	Result
Inhaling	Contracts and flattens	Contract	Raised (up and out)	Increased	Decreased	Air rushes in
Exhaling	Relaxes and returns to domed position	Relax	Lowered (down and in)	Decreased	Increased	Air is forced out

Worked example

Describe and explain what happens to a person's rate of breathing when they exercise.   [3 marks]

Answer
- During exercise more energy is required.
- As this energy is released by respiration more oxygen is required.
- To provide more oxygen, the person's breathing rate increases, as does the amount of air breathed in and out. An increased breathing rate also allows the extra carbon dioxide produced during exercise to be removed from the body.

Comparing the composition of inhaled and exhaled air

The table compares the composition of inhaled and exhaled air.

Gas	Inhaled air / %	Exhaled air / %	Why the change (if any)?
Oxygen	21	16	Oxygen diffuses from alveoli into blood and is used in respiration
Carbon dioxide	0.04	4	Carbon dioxide from respiration diffuses from blood into alveoli
Nitrogen	78	78	Nitrogen is not used in respiration

Respiration

Respiration is:

- a **chemical process**
- the release of energy for use in living organisms
- not breathing – all living things respire but not all living things breathe (e.g. plants respire but do not breathe).

The energy released can be used for many things including:

- movement
- growth and repair
- heat
- reproduction
- active transport.

The process of aerobic respiration can be summarised by the following word equation and balanced chemical equation:

glucose + oxygen $\rightarrow$ carbon dioxide + water + energy

$$C_6H_{12}O_6 + 6O_2 \rightarrow 6CO_2 + 6H_2O + energy\ (ATP)$$

Common features of respiratory surfaces

To improve the efficiency of respiration, many organisms have developed well adapted respiratory surfaces. In mammals, such as humans, lungs are present. In most plants, the leaves are the respiratory surface.

The table outlines the adaptations of gas-exchange surfaces.

Adaptation	Reason for adaptation
Large surface area	More opportunities for gases to be exchanged
Thin and permeable walls	Minimise diffusion distance and allow gases through
Moist	Allows gases to dissolve easily
Have features to maintain the concentration gradient, e.g. a diffusion gradient and (in mammals) a good blood supply	Ensure that gas exchange proceeds continuously

Aerobic and anaerobic respiration

Revised

Respiration with oxygen is called aerobic respiration and respiration in the absence of oxygen is called anaerobic respiration. The equations below summarise anaerobic respiration in yeast (the fungus used in brewing and baking) and in human muscle (during strenuous exercise).

Yeast:

glucose → ethanol + carbon dioxide + small amount of energy

Human:

glucose → lactic acid + small amount of energy

Revision Questions

Tested

1   Describe and explain three adaptations of the lungs that facilitate a high rate of gas exchange.   [6 marks]

2   Explain the difference between breathing and respiration.   [2 marks]

3   Name the parts of the respiratory system that air passes through as we breathe in, in the correct order ending in the alveoli.   [3 marks]

4   a) Describe the movement of the diaphragm and ribs as we breathe in.   [2 marks]

    b) How do these changes affect the volume of the chest cavity?   [1 mark]

5   State the differences between anaerobic respiration in muscle and yeast.   [2 marks]

6   Look at the diagram below:

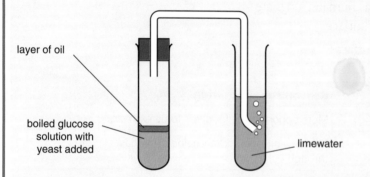

layer of oil

boiled glucose solution with yeast added

limewater

This apparatus can be used to investigate anaerobic respiration in yeast.

    a) Why is the glucose solution boiled?   [1 mark]

    b) What is the purpose of the layer of oil?   [1 mark]

    c) Give 2 changes that you would expect to occur as the experiment takes place.   [2 marks]

Go online for the answers

Online

6 The Nervous System and Hormones

Nerves and hormones are involved in sensing and responding to changes in the environment (stimuli). The action of nerves is faster and more short-lived than the action of hormones, which don't act as quickly and have longer lasting effects on the body.

Animal nervous system
Revised

The three components and basic sequence of sensing and responding to a stimulus are shown in Figure 6.1. The arrows linking the components represent nerve cells (neurones) that carry impulses (electrical messages) throughout the system.

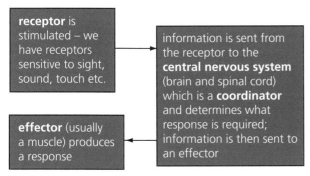

receptor is stimulated – we have receptors sensitive to sight, sound, touch etc.

information is sent from the receptor to the **central nervous system** (brain and spinal cord) which is a **coordinator** and determines what response is required; information is then sent to an effector

effector (usually a muscle) produces a response

↑ **Figure 6.1 Components of the nervous system**

The eye
Revised

The eye is an example of an advanced receptor – it contains a number of cell types that are sensitive to light. Figure 6.2 shows the structure of the eye and the role of the components in allowing vision.

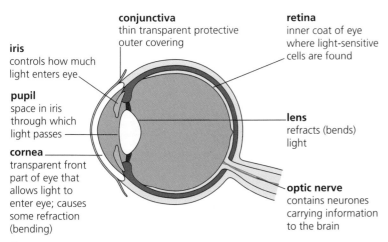

conjunctiva
thin transparent protective outer covering

retina
inner coat of eye where light-sensitive cells are found

iris
controls how much light enters eye

pupil
space in iris through which light passes

cornea
transparent front part of eye that allows light to enter eye; causes some refraction (bending)

lens
refracts (bends) light

optic nerve
contains neurones carrying information to the brain

↑ **Figure 6.2 Structure and function of the eye**

The clear fluid found in the front of the eye (**aqueous humour**) and in the back of the eye between the lens and the retina (**vitreous humour**) are needed to provide support to the eye and to allow light to pass through to the retina.

Controlling light levels entering the eye

The iris is the coloured part of the eye. It consists of two types of muscle: **radial** muscles which are like the spokes of a bicycle wheel, and **circular** muscle which forms rings around the pupil.

The table summarises the role of the iris muscles in controlling pupil size.

		Bright light	**Dim light**
Risk		Bright light can damage the cells of the retina leading to blindness	Low light levels can result in not enough light reaching the retina to form an image
Action of iris muscles	**Circular**	Contract	Relax
	Radial	Relax	Contract
Effect on pupil diameter		Decreased	Increased
Amount of light entering eye		Decreased	Increased

The eye and focusing Revised

Light is focused on the retina by changing the shape of the lens. This allows near and far objects to be seen clearly and is called **accommodation**.

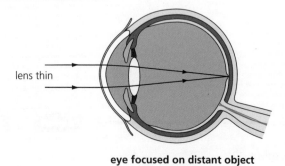

lens thin

eye focused on distant object

light rays arrive parallel; cornea refracts rays; lens is thin as little additional refraction is necessary to focus light on the retina

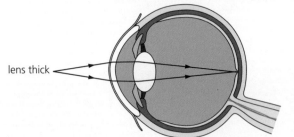

lens thick

eye focused on near object

light rays diverge; cornea refracts rays; lens is thicker as additional refraction is necessary to focus light on retina

⬆ Figure 6.3 Accommodation – focusing on far and near objects

To focus on a **near object** a ring of muscle surrounding the lens (ciliary body) contracts. This allows the suspensory ligaments to become loose and the lens bulges out as it is not under pressure.

When focussing on a **distant object**, the ciliary body relaxes. This causes suspensory ligaments to become taut, pulling the lens into a thinner flattened shape.

Worked example

The eye has the ability to adjust the size of the pupil in different light intensities.

a) Under what light condition is the pupil small? [1 mark]

b) Which muscles in the iris of the eye are responsible for this response? [2 marks]

c) Which of these two types of muscle is contracted when the pupil diameter is increased? [1 mark]

Answer

a) Bright light

b) Radial; circular

c) Radial

Neurones and synapses

Revised

Nerve cells (neurones) are specially adapted to carry electrical impulses through the nervous system. Their adaptations include:

- long length – to carry impulses long distances
- insulating sheath – to allow rapid transmission of impulses
- branching ends – to receive or pass impulses from or to many other nerve cells.

Synapses are the tiny gaps between nerve cells. For impulses to pass from one nerve cell to the next a transmitter chemical must diffuse across the synapse at a high enough concentration to trigger an impulse in the next cell.

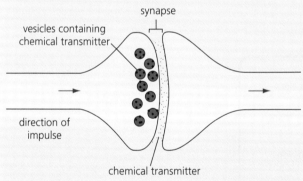

↑ **Figure 6.4 A synapse**

Voluntary and reflex actions

Our nervous system allows two basic types of response. The first of these are the **voluntary actions** – we have conscious control over these. The second type of responses are **reflex actions** – we are not conscious of these actions. Reflex actions tend to be much faster as they use a special pathway of nerves called the **reflex arc** that does not include 'thinking time'. The rapid nature of reflex actions means that many are used by the body as a means of protection.

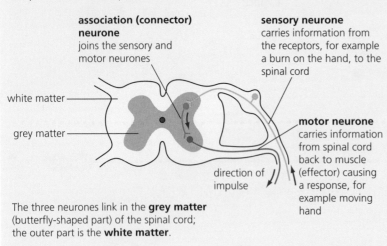

association (connector) neurone
joins the sensory and motor neurones

sensory neurone
carries information from the receptors, for example a burn on the hand, to the spinal cord

white matter

grey matter

motor neurone
carries information from spinal cord back to muscle (effector) causing a response, for example moving hand

direction of impulse

The three neurones link in the **grey matter** (butterfly-shaped part) of the spinal cord; the outer part is the **white matter**.

↑ **Figure 6.5 The reflex arc**

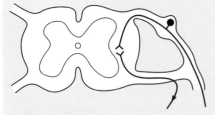

↑ **Figure 6.6 Incorrect diagram of a reflex arc**

> ### Exam tip
> When asked to complete reflex arcs, candidates often make mistakes (see Figure 6.6):
> - neurones drawn only in the white matter in the spinal cord – they should cross in to the grey matter
> - association (connector) neurone should not join with the other neurones – there should be a small gap at each end
> - motor neurone drawn leaving the spinal column in the wrong place – it should leave along the same route as the sensory neurone.

Hormones

Hormones are chemicals produced by special glands in the body that can travel through the blood to target specific organs in order to produce changes in the way the cells in the organ function.

Control of blood glucose levels

The role of insulin

The key hormone in the control of blood glucose levels is insulin. Although glucose is needed for respiration, high blood glucose levels can result in damage to cells.

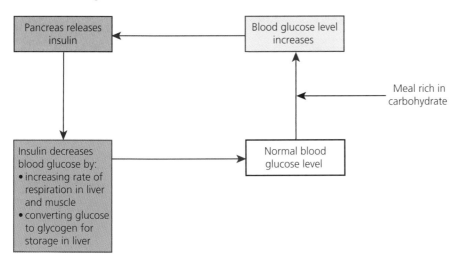

↑ **Figure 6.7 How blood glucose levels are controlled by negative feedback**

The mechanism that insulin uses to control blood glucose levels involves **negative feedback**. The action of insulin in reducing blood glucose levels means that less insulin is needed. When normal blood glucose levels are restored (due to the action of insulin), the pancreas no longer releases insulin.

The role of glucagon

A second hormone called glucagon is involved in increasing blood sugar levels during exercise or when blood glucose levels fall. Glucagon acts on the cells of the liver, causing them to convert glycogen back into glucose.

Diabetes

Diabetes is the condition where people fail to produce enough insulin or their cells fail to respond to it correctly.

Symptoms of diabetes include: high blood glucose levels, glucose in the urine, excessive thirst, lethargy (tiredness) and a frequent need to urinate.

Long-term dangers of diabetes if it is left untreated include: kidney damage, eye damage, stroke and heart disease.

The number of people with diabetes is increasing for a variety of reasons including poor diet, obesity and lack of exercise.

> **Exam tip**
>
> People with diabetes must test their blood glucose levels and may need to inject insulin to correct them if the levels are too high. Insulin cannot be eaten in a tablet form as the hormone would be digested in the stomach. If too much insulin is taken or if enough food is not eaten at regular intervals, blood glucose levels can fall too low resulting in a 'hypo' (hypoglycaemic attack) and unconsciousness.

Plants are also capable of responding to stimuli, for example the response of a plant to light. Parts of a plant above the ground most often grow towards light as this should increase the rate of growth as more photosynthesis can occur. This effect is known as **phototropism**. The hormone responsible for phototropism is called **auxin**. Phototropism is caused by auxin accumulating on the shaded side of a shoot and this causes more growth on that side.

The way auxins act is shown in Figure 6.8.

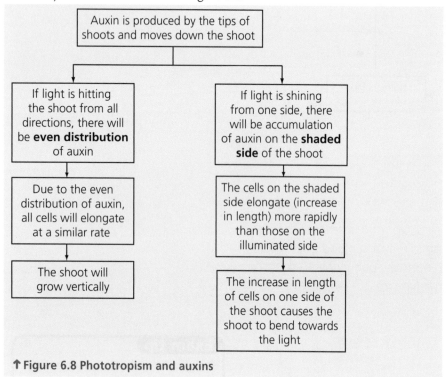

↑ **Figure 6.8 Phototropism and auxins**

Commercial uses of plant hormones

Many plant hormones are now synthetically produced and used in a number of ways as described in the table.

Use	How it works	Benefits
Selective weedkillers	Hormone stimulates such a high rate of uncontrolled growth that plant disintegrates	The hormones used only act on broadleaved plants (weeds) but not on narrow leaved grasses and cereals
Rooting powder	Hormone stimulates certain cells to develop the features of root cells	Can be used in horticulture to allow growth of new plants from cuttings
Promoting flower and fruit formation	Action of hormone causes flowers to develop – these flowers can then be pollinated to allow development of seeds and fruits	Allows more fruit to be produced, e.g. if there are adverse weather conditions or a lack of natural pollinators. Can also be used to produce seedless fruits
Tissue culture	Hormones can be used to stimulate the growth of all types of plant cell from a mass of cells called a callus	Allows species of plant that are rare or very difficult to breed to be produced more readily

1 **a)** In humans, In what form is glucose stored in the liver?

   b) What hormone results in glucose being stored in this form?

   c) In what organ is this hormone produced?   [3 marks]

2 Describe the changes that occur in the eye when it changes focus from a distant to a nearby object.   [3 marks]

3 **a)** Suggest which part of a plant is sensitive to light.

   b) Name the plant hormone responsible for causing directional growth.

   c) Describe how this hormone results in the growth of shoots towards light.

   d) What is this process called?   [4 marks]

4 The diagram shows the structure of the eye.

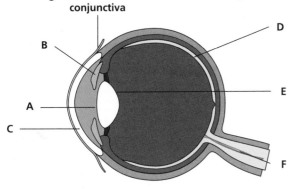

↑ **Figure 6.9 Structure and function of the eye**

   a) Name parts A–F shown in the diagram.   [6 marks]

   b) What is the function of part E?   [1 mark]

5 Place the following terms in the correct order:

   coordinator, stimulus, effector, receptor, response   [1 mark]

7 Ecological Relationships and Energy Flow

In order to understand ecology an understanding of the following terminology is required:

- **biodiversity** – a measure of the range of different species of organisms living in an area
- **community** – the relationships between all the living species in an area
- **ecosystem** – the relationship between the living species and their environment
- **environment** – the surroundings in which an organism lives
- **habitat** – the place where an organism lives and breeds
- **population** – the number of organisms of a single species in a given habitat.

Studying the environment   Revised

To study the environment effectively a range of sampling techniques can be used. Some techniques make use of apparatus that can be used to measure **biotic** (living) data, e.g. the distribution of plant or animal species. Examples of such apparatus and how they can be used are outlined in the table. Correct use of sampling techniques should allow the investigation of changes in distribution, e.g. from a hedgerow into the centre of a field, and also indicate levels of biodiversity.

Apparatus	Notes on use
stones to prevent rain flooding the trap or birds or other predators from removing the trapped animals jar or pot sunk in a hole in the ground pitfall trap	A hole is dug to accommodate a container and a raised lid is placed on top to prevent entry of rain/predators. The trap is then left for a period of time (e.g. 24 hours). Useful for collecting small ground-living animals such as beetles
quadrat	This is a square frame of sides 1 m or 50 cm that can be placed at a series of randomly chosen coordinates. The abundance of plant species is often measured in this way – if individual plants cannot be identified (e.g. grass) then percentage cover can be used. Can also be used for non-mobile animal species such as barnacles, limpets
pooter	A pooter allows small animals to be sucked into an observation chamber so that they can be more easily identified
net	Often used in long vegetation or in streams and rivers to catch small organisms for the purposes of identification

Abiotic factors

To understand an ecosystem fully, the **abiotic** (non-living) factors in the environment must also be measured. These factors and how they are measured include light intensity (use e.g. light meter to measure), temperature (e.g. thermometer), wind speed (e.g. anemometer), water availability (e.g. rain gauge, or dry a soil sample to calculate its percentage moisture) and pH (e.g. pH meter or soil-testing kit or probe). Other factors that affect the numbers of organisms living in an area are the extent of cultivation (if ground is managed there are likely to be fewer species present – therefore lower biodiversity), space, shelter, presence of individuals to mate with, predators and mineral availability for plants.

Classification
Revised

It can sometimes be a challenge to correctly identify organisms during field work. A key is often used to identify plants or animals but keys also allow organisms to be classified. Classification allows a better understanding of evolution, biodiversity and how best to conserve species for future generations.

You should know the features of the following groups of organisms:

1 **Chordates** – animals with backbones: mammals, reptiles, fish, amphibians, birds (MRFAB)

2 **Insects** – animals with an exoskeleton and a body divided into three sections (head, thorax and abdomen), two pairs of wings, three pairs of jointed legs, body temperature not constant

3 **Annelids** – animals with a segmented body, and hairlike structures called chaetae for grip, body temperature not constant

4 **Flowering plants** – plants with true roots, stems and a highly developed transport (vascular) system. Rely on flower, seed and fruit production to facilitate reproduction.

The five kingdoms

The table summarises the key features of the five kingdoms of organisms.

Group	Nutrition	Cell wall	Cellular organisation
Protoctista	Saprophytic or photosynthetic	Cellulose / no cell wall	Single-celled with nucleus / algae that are not truly multicellular
Bacteria	Saprophytic	Non-cellulose	Single-celled, lacking a nucleus
Fungi	Saprophytic or parasitic	Non-cellulose	Single or multicellular, sometimes difficult to distinguish cells and so are referred to as acellular
Plants	Photosynthetic	Cellulose	Multicellular
Animals	Heterotrophic	None	Multicellular

Exam tip

You should be aware of the following.
- Protoctista is a kingdom containing organisms that can be hard to classify – e.g. some organisms have both plant and animal characteristics.
- Saprophytic nutrition is a form of external digestion – enzymes act outside the organism and the products of digestion are then absorbed.
- Viruses pose a big problem for biologists as they can only reproduce through invading host cells. For this reason they are hard to classify as true living organisms.

Some organisms are very similar e.g. horses and donkeys – but how are they classified into different species? The answer is if they can breed to produce fertile offspring and look similar then they are the same species.

A male donkey and a female horse can breed to produce a mule but mules are infertile and therefore horses and donkeys are different species.

Changes in population
Revised

The size of a population in an ecosystem is governed by birth and death rates as well as immigration (the arrival of new members of a species from another ecosystem) and emigration (movement of members of a species out of the ecosystem).

These factors can be used to estimate a change in population size through the use of the following mathematical relationship:

change in population size = (birth rate + immigration) – (death rate + emigration)

> **Exam tip**
>
> Most population questions do not involve emigration or immigration. It is therefore important to know that if there is:
>
> no population change, then number of births = number of deaths
>
> population decrease, then birth rate is < death rate
>
> population increase, then birth rate is > death rate

Transfer of energy
Revised ✓

As plants are capable of photosynthesis they are able to harness the Sun's energy and use this to produce food for themselves and other organisms that consume them. The flow of energy from plants to other organisms can be represented in food chains, as shown in the example in Figure 7.1.

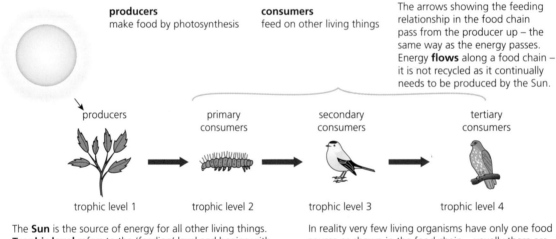

producers
make food by photosynthesis

consumers
feed on other living things

The arrows showing the feeding relationship in the food chain pass from the producer up – the same way as the energy passes. Energy **flows** along a food chain – it is not recycled as it continually needs to be produced by the Sun.

producers | primary consumers | secondary consumers | tertiary consumers

trophic level 1 | trophic level 2 | trophic level 3 | trophic level 4

The **Sun** is the source of energy for all other living things. **Trophic level** refers to the 'feeding' level and begins with producers as level 1.

In reality very few living organisms have only one food source as shown in the food chain – usually there are many interlinked organisms as in a **food web**.

↑ **Figure 7.1 A food chain – a chain of living organisms through which energy passes**

Pyramids of numbers and biomass

A **pyramid of numbers** is a simple diagram used to represent the numbers of organisms at each trophic level. It is common that there is a decrease in the numbers of organisms as the food chain progresses from producers to the top consumer (for example in Figure 7.1 there would be many more plants than there would be birds of prey at the end of the chain).

In some cases a pyramid of numbers can become atypical as one producer could provide food for many primary consumers. An example of this can be seen in roses where a single bush can sustain hundreds of aphids (greenfly). Both typical and atypical pyramids of number are shown in Figure 7.2.

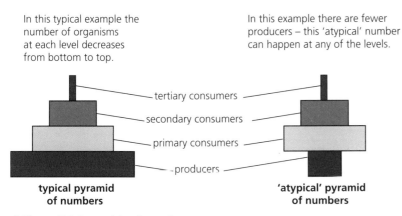

In this typical example the number of organisms at each level decreases from bottom to top.

In this example there are fewer producers – this 'atypical' number can happen at any of the levels.

tertiary consumers
secondary consumers
primary consumers
producers

typical pyramid of numbers

'atypical' pyramid of numbers

⬆ Figure 7.2 Pyramids of numbers

> **Exam tip**
>
> You should be aware that it is very difficult to produce pyramids for organisms that feed at two different tropic levels.

A **pyramid of biomass** is a diagram used to represent the mass of living material at each trophic level. In our example there would be much more living material in the rose bush than the aphids, so the steps of the pyramids always become shorter as you progress through the food chain.

> **Exam tip**
>
> You may be asked to draw pyramids from data provided in a question or to complete a pyramid of biomass having been given a pyramid of numbers. To make sure that you gain as many marks as possible, stick to these basic guidelines:
> - never change the order of the food chain – the producer is always at the bottom and the final consumer at the top
> - keep it symmetrical
> - bars should all have the same depth
> - if required, ensure you use an appropriate scale for the length of bars (usually an indication of scale is provided in questions)
> - if converting from an atypical pyramid of numbers to pyramid of biomass remember that the pyramids of biomass are always 'proper' pyramids.

Why food chains are so short

Revised

Food chains never exceed four or five trophic levels because not all energy from one trophic level is transferred to the next. The reasons for this are:

- respiration of organisms at each stage releases heat energy that cannot be passed on through feeding

- excreted waste contains some energy

- faeces also contain energy that cannot be digested

- not all parts of the organism can be eaten.

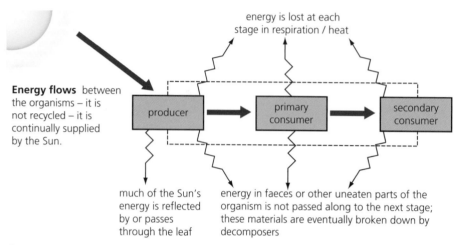

Energy flows between the organisms – it is not recycled – it is continually supplied by the Sun.

energy is lost at each stage in respiration / heat

producer → primary consumer → secondary consumer

much of the Sun's energy is reflected by or passes through the leaf

energy in faeces or other uneaten parts of the organism is not passed along to the next stage; these materials are eventually broken down by decomposers

↑ **Figure 7.3 How energy is lost in a food chain**

From Figure 7.3 we can see that short food chains are more efficient: there are fewer opportunities for energy to be lost. For this reason, countries with large populations or those suffering from famine have food chains with only one consumer, for example:

rice → human

Nutrient cycles

Revised

Living organisms rely on a number of key elements. In living systems, carbon, nitrogen and other elements are recycled through many processes that are dependent on the presence of certain bacteria and fungi.

Decomposition is a key process in the recycling of carbon and nitrogen. The decay process releases the nutrients back into the soil. The bacteria and fungi responsible for this recycling feed on dead plant and animal material as well as waste materials released by egestion and excretion of animals.

The result is the formation of **humus** – a component of the soil in which plants grow and from which they extract minerals. For this to happen, the bacteria and fungi involved release digestive enzymes on to the material. Following this **extracellular digestion** (meaning outside the body or cell) the soluble products are absorbed by the organism.

The carbon cycle

As shown in Figure 7.4, there are a number of processes responsible for the cycling of carbon.

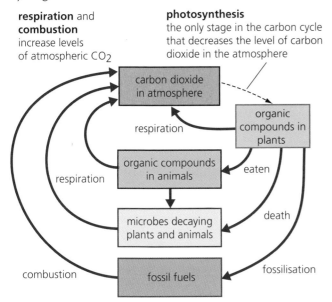

respiration and **combustion** increase levels of atmospheric CO_2

photosynthesis the only stage in the carbon cycle that decreases the level of carbon dioxide in the atmosphere

carbon dioxide in atmosphere

organic compounds in plants

respiration

organic compounds in animals

eaten

respiration

microbes decaying plants and animals

death

combustion

fossil fuels

fossilisation

↑ **Figure 7.4 The carbon cycle**

In very simple terms, the amount of carbon dioxide in our atmosphere should stay constant, *but* if the amount of respiration and combustion of fossil fuels increases and the amount of photosynthesis decreases (due to, for example, deforestation), then levels of carbon dioxide will increase. There is a vast amount of scientific evidence to suggest that human activities have resulted in increased carbon dioxide levels which have, in turn, led to the greenhouse effect and global warming. Although there is much evidence to support this theory it should be remembered that there are other possible explanations for some of the increase of global temperature, such as natural variations in temperatures due to solar activity.

Abiotic data used to monitor global warning includes carbon dioxide levels, extent and size of polar icefields, ice density and sea levels.

In light of the increased levels of carbon dioxide in the atmosphere, governments have put in place policies at national and local levels to reduce carbon emissions through placing a greater emphasis on use of renewable energy sources, and changes in agricultural practices.

The nitrogen cycle

Nitrogen is needed by all living organisms to make proteins. The major processes involved in the nitrogen cycle are shown in Figure 7.5. The processes of nitrification and nitrogen fixation rely on aerobic conditions (oxygen must be available). Waterlogged soils have reduced oxygen levels – this is why flooding can be a problem for farmers growing crops.

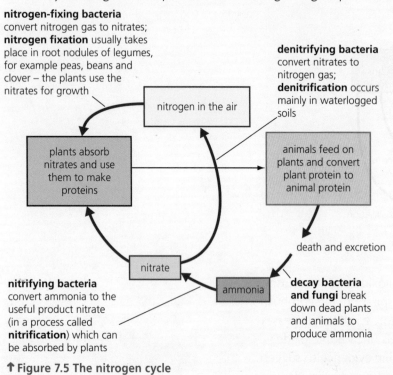

nitrogen-fixing bacteria convert nitrogen gas to nitrates; **nitrogen fixation** usually takes place in root nodules of legumes, for example peas, beans and clover – the plants use the nitrates for growth

denitrifying bacteria convert nitrates to nitrogen gas; **denitrification** occurs mainly in waterlogged soils

nitrogen in the air

plants absorb nitrates and use them to make proteins

animals feed on plants and convert plant protein to animal protein

death and excretion

nitrate

ammonia

nitrifying bacteria convert ammonia to the useful product nitrate (in a process called **nitrification**) which can be absorbed by plants

decay bacteria and fungi break down dead plants and animals to produce ammonia

↑ **Figure 7.5 The nitrogen cycle**

Worked example

The build up of carbon dioxide in our atmosphere has been linked to global warming.

a) Suggest two measures that could be taken to reduce carbon dioxide emissions. [2 marks]

b) Copy and complete the following table about the nitrogen cycle. [4 marks]

Process	Details
i)	Results in the conversion of nitrogen gas into nitrates
Denitrification	ii)
iii)	Ammonia containing compounds are converted into nitrate
iv)	Nitrogen containing compounds are released from dead organisms

Answers

a) use of renewable energy (wind, solar, hydroelectric – or other suitable suggestion); make greater use of public transport / reduced used of cars

b) i) nitrogen fixation; ii) nitrates converted into nitrogen gas; iii) nitrification; iv) decomposition/decay

Minerals

Three major minerals are required for healthy growth in plants:

● **magnesium** for making **chlorophyll**

● **calcium** for the production of new **cell walls**

● **nitrogen** in the form of nitrates for the formation of **protein**.

For effective absorption of these minerals from the soil, plants have **root hair cells**. These are cells with an extended cell wall that increases the surface area for absorption of minerals and water.

To improve the growth of their crops, farmers may add fertilisers to their soil.

Fertilisers can be natural or artificial and are designed to increase the levels of the minerals magnesium, calcium and nitrogen and other minerals.

Natural fertilisers	Artificial fertilisers
e.g. manure, compost ● low cost ● release nutrients throughout the growing season and do not leach easily ● amounts of minerals contained in them can vary ● they can be difficult to store and spread	● more expensive than natural fertilisers ● more easily applied to fields ● more accurate level of each mineral can be applied ● soluble and can leach easily leading to pollution ● for food to be labelled 'organic', only natural fertilisers can be used during growing

Mineral absorption

The absorption of minerals from the soil relies on a process called **active uptake**. This process uses **energy** to move the minerals from low concentration to high concentration (**against the concentration gradient**).

> ### Exam tip
>
> The energy required for active uptake is derived from respiration – oxygen is required. If soils become waterlogged then oxygen levels are too low to allow sufficient energy to be released. This, in turn, results in minerals not being absorbed and poor plant growth. Make sure that you can link all these aspects together in order to answer questions on active uptake of minerals from soil.

Eutrophication

Revised

Eutrophication is a form of water pollution and can be the result of sewage entering waterways. It is a problem associated with the incorrect use of all fertilisers. The additional nutrients provided result in the sequence of events outlined in Figure 7.6.

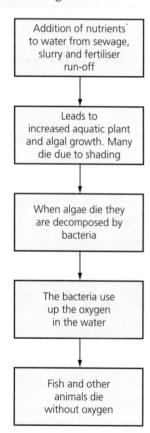

Addition of nutrients to water from sewage, slurry and fertiliser run-off

↓

Leads to increased aquatic plant and algal growth. Many die due to shading

↓

When algae die they are decomposed by bacteria

↓

The bacteria use up the oxygen in the water

↓

Fish and other animals die without oxygen

↑ **Figure 7.6 Summary of eutrophication**

Acid rain

Revised

In addition to the effects of global warming, the combustion of fossil fuels can lead to the production of acid rain due to the release of sulfur dioxide and nitrogen oxides. The flow diagram in Figure 7.7 summarises the production of acid rain.

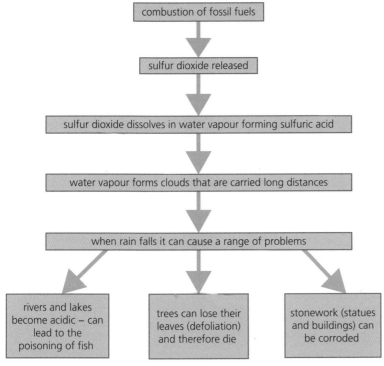

Exam tip

The problems caused by acid rain are often not seen in the country that released the original pollutant as the prevailing winds carry the rain clouds long distances before the rain falls and causes the problems described. International action has now been taken to filter emissions from combustion of fuels and the increased use of renewable energy such as solar, wind and hydroelectric power has vastly reduced the emission of the gases that cause acid rain.

↑ **Figure 7.7 Acid rain production and effects**

Monitoring environmental change

Revised

It is easy to measure factors such as oxygen, carbon dioxide and pollutant levels by taking samples and using chemical tests but the distribution of certain species of plants and animals (**indicator species**) can be more useful to biologists when studying the environment. Examples of indicator species are shown in the table.

Indicator species	Explanation
Lichen	Lichens are simple plants that cannot tolerate air pollution. Their presence on brick, stone and roofing indicates low levels of pollution. They are rarely found in towns and cities where air pollution is high
Bloodworms	These water-dwelling animals can only survive when oxygen levels are low. They are therefore good indicators of instances of eutrophication

Revision Questions

Tested

1 Name and describe how to use a piece of apparatus that could be used to sample insects and other small animals living on the forest floor. **[4 marks]**

2 Outline the unique features of each of the following groups of organisms:

a) plants **[1 mark]**

b) bacteria. **[2 marks]**

3 Explain why, in terms of energy, it is better for humans to feed on corn than on chicken. **[3 marks]**

4 State the name of the only process in the carbon cycle that takes carbon dioxide out of the atmosphere. **[1 mark]**

5 Outline the roles of each of the following types of bacteria in the nitrogen cycle:

a) nitrogen fixing

b) denitrifying

c) nitrifying. **[3 marks]**

6 State one advantage and one disadvantage for each of using:

a) natural

b) artificial fertilisers. **[4 marks]**

Go online for the answers

Online

8 Osmosis and Plant Transport

Osmosis is the movement of water from a dilute solution to a stronger solution through a **selectively permeable membrane**.

selectively permeable membrane – allows small molecules through (water) but not larger molecules (sugar)

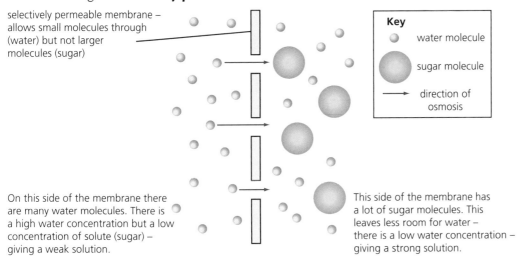

Key

○ water molecule

○ sugar molecule

→ direction of osmosis

On this side of the membrane there are many water molecules. There is a high water concentration but a low concentration of solute (sugar) – giving a weak solution.

This side of the membrane has a lot of sugar molecules. This leaves less room for water – there is a low water concentration – giving a strong solution.

↑ **Figure 8.1 The process of osmosis**

> **Exam tip**
>
> In Figure 8.1 the water moves from left to right by osmosis. Exam questions often give examples of osmosis and ask you to explain what is happening.

The following questions show two ways in which osmosis is examined.

Worked example

1   The apparatus shown was set up in a classroom to demonstrate the process of osmosis. Describe and explain what happens after 24 hours. [3 marks]

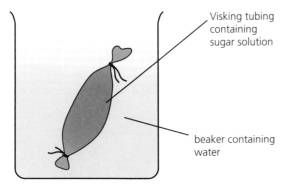

Visking tubing containing sugar solution

beaker containing water

2   Five potato cylinders each measuring 40 mm were placed in concentrated salt solution for 24 hours. When they were re-measured their average length was 37 mm. Explain this result. [3 marks]

Answers

1   The following three points for 3 marks.

  ● There are more water molecules outside than inside the tubing.

  ● Water would move into the tubing and the tubing would expand.

  ● The Visking tubing is selectively permeable.

2   Three of the four following points for 3 marks.

  ● There was more water in the cells of the potato than in the concentrated salt solution. You could also say that the salt solution is more concentrated than the potato.

  ● Water moved from the potato into the concentrated salt solution.

  ● By osmosis.

  ● Through a selectively permeable membrane.

Exam tip

You had to work out that the sugar solution inside the Visking tubing would contain fewer water molecules than the water outside. Figure 8.1 shows why this is so.

You would not get a mark for using the word 'osmosis' in your answer because it was mentioned in the question.

Exam tip

This time you would get 1 mark for using the word 'osmosis'.

Osmosis and plants

Revised

Normally a plant cell is more concentrated than its surroundings:

● **Water** enters the cell by **osmosis**.

● The vacuole expands pushing the cell membrane against the cell wall.

● This causes the **turgor** necessary for support.

● The **cell wall** stops the membrane expanding too far to cause damage and therefore limits the water intake.

If a plant cell is surrounded by a more concentrated solution (this very seldom happens in nature) the cell will **lose water** by **osmosis**.

The cell loses turgor and the membrane will pull away from the cell wall as the vacuole shrinks. This is **plasmolysis**.

Animal cells, e.g. red blood cells, do not have a cell wall – if they take in too much water they will burst (**lysis**).

Plants use water for:

● **support** (turgor)

● **transpiration** – the movement of water up through a plant, **evaporation** from leaf cells followed by **diffusion** out of the **stomata**

● **transport** – as water moves up through a plant it carries **minerals**

● water is a raw material of **photosynthesis**.

The bubble potometer

The rate of water loss can be measured or compared in different conditions by a **potometer** as shown in Figure 8.2. This apparatus measures the **water uptake** by a cut shoot. It does not accurately measure the exact amount of transpiration (water loss through the leaves) as some of the water entering the leaves is used and does not evaporate, but it is an excellent method of **comparing** transpiration in different conditions.

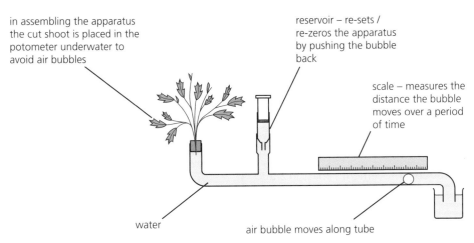

in assembling the apparatus the cut shoot is placed in the potometer underwater to avoid air bubbles

reservoir – re-sets / re-zeros the apparatus by pushing the bubble back

scale – measures the distance the bubble moves over a period of time

water

air bubble moves along tube

Figure 8.2 The potometer

The weighing method

We can compare rates of transpiration by measuring the loss in mass of a pot plant (or shoot in a flask) in different conditions. Normally the plant is placed on a top-pan balance for at least 24 hours and the mass recorded at intervals.

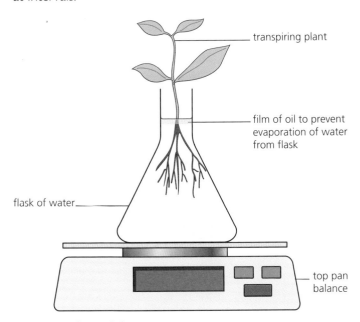

transpiring plant

film of oil to prevent evaporation of water from flask

flask of water

top pan balance

Figure 8.3 The weight potometer

Exam tip

Using the weighing method, it is important that water can only escape by transpiration (through the leaves) – the compost around the shoot must be covered by polythene to stop the evaporation of soil water.

Exam tip

As with the bubble potometer, the weighing method can only be used to *compare* rates of transpiration, not give absolute values – it is possible the pot plant could grow enough to partially offset the losses due to transpiration.

Factors affecting rate of transpiration

As the following environmental factors all affect the rate of evaporation of water from leaves they also affect the transpiration rate.

● **Temperature**: in warmer conditions water evaporates faster.

● **Wind speed**: evaporation is faster in higher wind speeds as the wind rapidly removes the evaporating water away from the stomata and leaf surface thus maintaining a steep gradient of moisture.

● **Humidity**: humid conditions restrict evaporation as there is a decrease in moisture gradient between the leaf surface and the surrounding air.

The **surface area of leaves** (or number of leaves) affects the rate at which transpiration takes place, as the greater the surface area the greater the number of stomata and the faster evaporation takes place.

> ### Exam tip
> A common exam question asks you to state how you would use a potometer to measure the rate of transpiration in different conditions. Marks are likely to be available for:
> ● describing how you create the different conditions, e.g. using a polythene bag around the plant to produce humid conditions
> ● calculating rate – measuring both bubble movement / mass loss and the time period
> ● controlling other variables.

1   You are given two solutions. One solution is 5% sucrose and the other is 10% sucrose but they are not labelled. You are also provided with Visking tubing and a top-pan balance and any other standard laboratory equipment you might require.

Plan an investigation that will allow you to identify the sugar solutions.   [4 marks]

2   a)   The following data have been obtained from an investigation using a weight potometer to compare the rate of transpiration in windy and still conditions. A fan was used to create windy conditions.

	Still conditions	Windy conditions
Mass of pot plant at start / g	460	490
Mass of pot plant after 24 hrs / g	437	392
Change of mass	23	98
% change of mass	5	

   i)   Calculate the percentage change in mass in windy conditions.   [2 marks]

   ii)   Why is it important to calculate percentage change of mass rather than just use change in mass?   [1 mark]

   iii) Give three variables you would have to keep constant in this experiment.   [3 marks]

   iv)   Describe and explain the results of the investigation.   [1 mark]

   b) i)   Describe how turgor occurs.   [2 marks]

   ii)   Describe the appearance of a turgid plant cell when viewed by a microscope.   [2 marks]

3   a)   An investigation into osmosis was carried out with carrot cylinders. Three test tubes (**A, B and C**) were set up and different solutions were added as described in the table below. A carrot cylinder of 50 mm length was placed in each of the test tubes and the tubes were left for 2 hours before the cylinders were surface-dried and re-weighed.

Test tube	Solution	Length of carrot cylinder / mm	
		at start	after 2 hours
A	concentrated sugar solution	50	46
B	dilute sugar solution	50	50
C	water	50	52

   i)   Explain the results for test tubes **A** and **B**.   [4 marks]

   ii)   Give **two** reasons why it would be more accurate to measure change in mass (as opposed to change in cylinder length) in this experiment.   [2 marks]

   iii) Give **one** factor that should be kept constant in this experiment.   [1 mark]

   b) Give **two** functions of water in plants.   [2 marks]

Go online for the answers   Online

9 Chromosomes, Genes and DNA

Four key facts

1 The genetic material (**DNA**, deoxyribonucleic acid) is contained in **chromosomes** in the nucleus of the cell.

2 Chromosomes occur as **functional pairs** (except in sex cells).

3 **Genes** are short sections of chromosomes that control specific characteristics.

4 **Genes** are therefore **short lengths of DNA**.

The structure of DNA

Revised

Figure 9.1 shows the structure of DNA.

DNA consists of two **phosphate** and **sugar** (deoxyribose) strands held together by **bases** linked by hydrogen bonds. This unit is repeated along the length of the DNA molecule.

DNA is the code-carrying part of genes and chromosomes that determines how individuals develop.

The four bases can combine only in the order:
• adenine–thymine
• guanine–cytosine.
Note: In the model only A–T or T–A and C–G or G–C combinations exist. These combinations are referred to as **base pairing**.

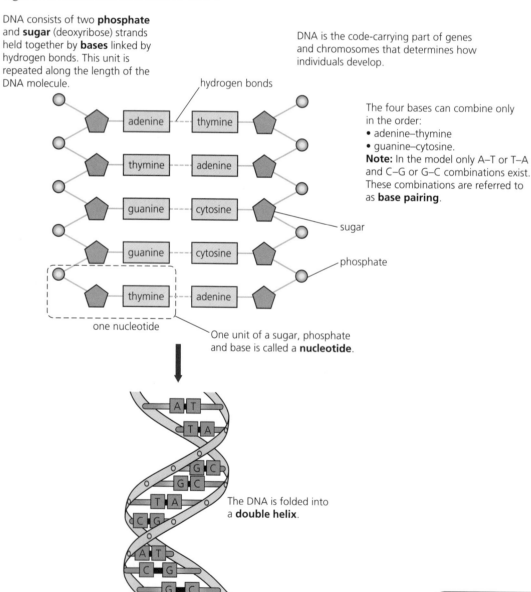

↑ **Figure 9.1 The structure of DNA**

The **sequence** of bases (along the length of each chromosome) in each individual is **unique**.

Exam tip

The sequence of bases that makes each individual unique is the sequence along **one** strand (the coding strand) of the DNA.

Deoxyribose nucleic acid works by coding for different amino acids which then combine to form proteins, as shown in Figure 9.2.

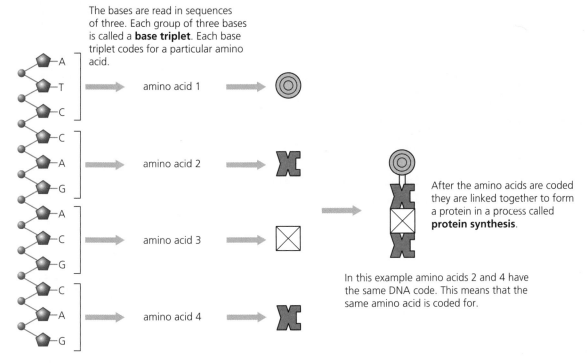

The bases are read in sequences of three. Each group of three bases is called a **base triplet**. Each base triplet codes for a particular amino acid.

amino acid 1

amino acid 2

amino acid 3

amino acid 4

After the amino acids are coded they are linked together to form a protein in a process called **protein synthesis**.

In this example amino acids 2 and 4 have the same DNA code. This means that the same amino acid is coded for.

Only one strand of the DNA (the coding strand) is involved in the coding process.

↑ **Figure 9.2 How DNA works**

Worked example

a) A length of DNA consists of 180 bases. How many amino acids does this section code for? Explain your answer.   [3 marks]

b) In the same section 60 of the bases are thymine. How many guanine bases are there in the section?   [3 marks]

Answers

a) 30; only half the bases (90) are in the coding strand; in the coding strand each sequence of three bases (a triplet) produces one amino acid.

b) If 60 bases are thymine then 60 bases are adenine; A and T always code together (total 120); remaining 60 must be 30 guanine and 30 cytosine (C and G always code together).

The diagram shows the contribution made by the key scientists – using different investigative methods – in working out the structure of DNA.

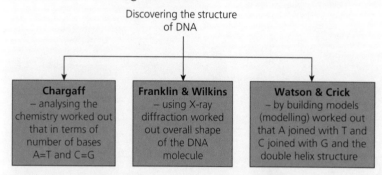

The discovery of DNA is an example of the **collaborative nature of science** – the way in which scientists can work together to make new discoveries through building up information in stages. New scientific knowledge is validated by **peer review** – other scientists checking research to ensure that new discoveries are based on experiments that are valid and reliable.

Revision Questions ─────────────── Tested

1   The following diagram shows a short section of DNA.

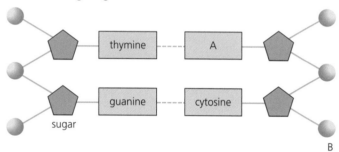

a) Identify A and B.   [2 marks]

b) What is meant by the 'unique nature of an individual's DNA'?   [1 mark]

c) Explain the base triplet hypothesis.   [2 marks]

2   Working out the structure of DNA was an excellent example of the collaborative nature of science. Using this example explain what is meant by the 'collaborative nature of science'.   [2 marks]

3   The following table shows the percentage of different bases in the DNA of two different organisms.

| Bases | adenine | guanine | cytosine | thymine |
Organism	%	%	%	%
A	40		10	
B		17		

a) Copy and complete the table.   [3 marks]

b) Outline the structure of the double helix.   [2 marks]

4   **a)** Place the following structures in order of size starting with the smallest.   [1 mark]

chromosome : cell : nucleus : gene : base

b) Describe how DNA codes for protein.   [3 marks]

Go online for the answers ─────────────── Online

10 Cell Division and Genetics

Measuring growth

Humans are typically measured by their **height** and **mass**.

Measurements of growth for other organisms include:

Method	Advantages	Disadvantages
Cell length	Easy to measure	● Irregular shape / size ● No reference to cell number
Number of cells	Usually accurate representation of size	● Difficult to count if organism large ● No account of different cell sizes
Dry mass	Very accurate indicator of amount of organic material	● Time consuming ● Organism killed during drying

Mitosis and meiosis

Mitosis and **meiosis** are types of cell division involved in growth and development.

Mitosis

● takes place **throughout body**

● important in **growth** and **replacing worn out / damaged cells**

● ensures that all new cells have exactly the **same chromosome arrangement** as each other and as the parent cell.

Meiosis

● occurs in **sex organs** (testes and ovaries) only

● produces **gametes**

● is **reduction division** as produces gametes with half the number of chromosomes (**haploid number**) as other cells (**diploid number**) – ensures that when gametes fuse in fertilisation the normal diploid number is restored

● with either chromosome in a pair of chromosomes combining with either of another pair of chromosomes in gamete formation (and so on for all 23 pair in humans) this ensures that there are millions of possibilities of chromosome arrangements in the gametes from one person – this **independent assortment** is a major cause of variation in individuals.

The differences between mitosis and meiosis are summarised in Figure 10.1 on page 60.

> **Exam tip**
> **h**alf for **h**aploid

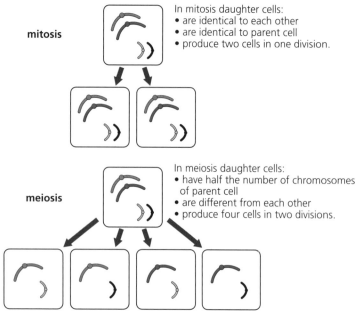

In mitosis daughter cells:
- are identical to each other
- are identical to parent cell
- produce two cells in one division.

In meiosis daughter cells:
- have half the number of chromosomes of parent cell
- are different from each other
- produce four cells in two divisions.

↑ Figure 10.1 The differences between mitosis and meiosis (only two pairs of chromosomes are shown)

Asexual reproduction
Revised

Common in plants – this produces **clones** by **mitosis** without the need of producing gametes by meiosis.

Tissue cloning is a type of cloning that involves treating small sections of plants with hormones to produce new plants. It has many advantages:

● can be carried out in a lab all year round

● can produce many thousand identical plants from one 'parent'

● can produce disease-free plants if the procedure is carried out in sterile conditions

● can be used to conserve rare varieties.

Cancer
Revised

Cancer is uncontrolled cell division.

Causes of cancer are summarised below:

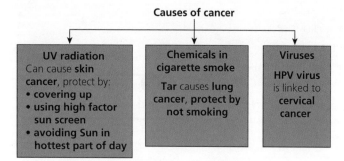

Causes of cancer

| UV radiation | Chemicals in cigarette smoke | Viruses |

UV radiation
Can cause **skin cancer**, protect by:
- **covering up**
- **using high factor sun screen**
- **avoiding Sun in hottest part of day**

Chemicals in cigarette smoke

Tar causes **lung cancer**, protect by not smoking

Viruses

HPV virus is linked to cervical cancer

Types of tumour

● **Benign** tumours do not spread through body – they often have a distinct boundary (are encapsulated).

● **Malignant** tumours – spread throughout body (not encapsulated).

Treatment options

Treatment of cancer depends on the type and location of the tumour and includes:

surgery – physically removing the cancer cells

radiotherapy – using X-rays or other radiation to kill the cancer cells

chemotherapy – using drugs to kill the cancer cells.

Screening programmes

Screening programmes are designed to detect cancer at the earliest possible stage – **before** the cancer becomes malignant and spreads through the body. This ensures that treatment has the best chance of success.

There are screening programmes for many types of cancer including breast and cervical cancer (women), testicular (men) and skin cancer.

Genetics

Genetics is the passing on of characteristics from parents to offspring. Chromosomes in the cell nucleus carry the genetic material in short sections called genes. Each gene carries the code for a particular characteristic, for example eye colour. As chromosomes occur in pairs each chromosome in a pair carries the same gene (for example for eye colour) but the gene for eye colour may have different forms (called alleles) in the two chromosomes (one allele may be for brown eyes and one for blue eyes). This is shown in Figure 10.2.

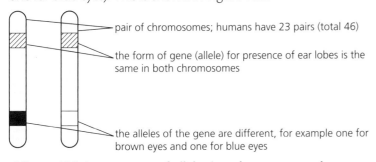

pair of chromosomes; humans have 23 pairs (total 46)

the form of gene (allele) for presence of ear lobes is the same in both chromosomes

the alleles of the gene are different, for example one for brown eyes and one for blue eyes

↑ **Figure 10.2 Arrangement of alleles in a chromosome pair**

Some of the key genetic terms are defined in the table.

Definitions of some important genetic terms

Term	Definition	Example
Gene	Short section of chromosome that codes for a particular characteristic	Gene for eye colour
Allele	A particular form of a gene	Brown eyes and blue eyes are different alleles of the eye colour gene
Homozygous	Both alleles of a gene are the same	Both alleles are for brown eyes
Heterozygous	Alleles of a gene are different	One allele is for brown eyes and the other is for blue eyes (Figure 10.2)

> **Exam tip**
>
> Genetics questions normally involve asking you to work out what the offspring are from particular parents (sometimes you are asked to work backwards and work out the parents).

Genetic crosses

Figure 10.3 shows how to set out the cross when you are asked to work out the offspring produced from two heterozygous parents using the example of height in peas. Peas can be either tall or dwarf and this is controlled by a single gene that has tall and dwarf alleles. A cross involving one characteristic (for example height) is a monohybrid cross.

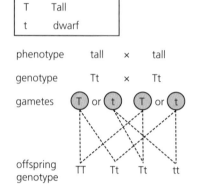

Key

T	Tall
t	dwarf

Either (but not both) of the two genotype alleles can pass into a gamete; in this example each parent produces equal numbers of T and t gametes.

There is an equal chance of either gamete from a parent combining with either gamete of the other parent; this produces the offspring in the ratio 3:1.

↑ **Figure 10.3 How to set out a cross when answering a genetics question**

Some other important terms that are in Figure 10.3 are defined in the table.

Term	Definition	Example
Genotype	Paired symbols showing the allele arrangement in an individual	Parents in Figure 10.3 have the genotype Tt
Phenotype	Outward appearance of an individual	Parents in Figure 10.3 have a tall phenotype
Dominant	In the heterozygous condition the dominant allele overrides the non-dominant (recessive) allele	Parents in Figure 10.3 are both tall even though they are heterozygous and have a dwarf allele
Recessive	Recessive allele is dominated by the dominant allele – it only shows itself in the phenotype if there are two recessive alleles	Only one-quarter of the offspring in the cross are dwarf as only one-quarter have no dominant T allele present

Exam tip

There are some other important points about genetic crosses that you need to know.

- It is very important to get the gametes correct. This is probably where most mistakes are made at GCSE level. Remember there is only one symbol in each gamete (only one chromosome and therefore one allele from a pair of chromosomes enters a gamete). If the parents are heterozygous then there are two possible types of gametes and if they are homozygous there is only one type of gamete.

- Ratios are only accurate when large numbers of offspring are involved. For example the 3:1 ratio in the earlier example may only be accurate if there are large numbers. This is because the mixing of gametes (and alleles) is entirely random during fertilisation.

- Sometimes the offspring are referred to as the **F1 generation** and if parents are described as **pure breeding** they will be homozygous.

- Crosses can also be worked out using **Punnett squares**.

Figure 10.4 shows how a Punnett square can be used. In this example, using height in peas as before, a heterozygote is crossed with a homozygous recessive pea.

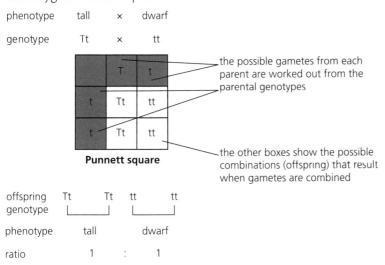

phenotype   tall   ×   dwarf

genotype   Tt   ×   tt

the possible gametes from each parent are worked out from the parental genotypes

Punnett square

the other boxes show the possible combinations (offspring) that result when gametes are combined

offspring   Tt   Tt   tt   tt
genotype

phenotype   tall   dwarf

ratio   1   :   1

↑ **Figure 10.4 How to use a Punnett square**

Worked example

Brown eyes are dominant to blue eyes. Using the symbols B = brown and b = blue show how brown-eyed parents can have children with blue eyes.   [4 marks]

Answer

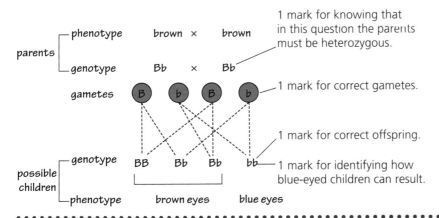

1 mark for knowing that in this question the parents must be heterozygous.

1 mark for correct gametes.

1 mark for correct offspring.

1 mark for identifying how blue-eyed children can result.

Individuals that are homozygous dominant or heterozygous have different genotypes but the same phenotype. The test cross can be used to determine the genotype of an individual of dominant phenotype but unknown genotype as shown in Figure 10.5.

In the example of the pea, a tall plant could be homozygous (TT) or heterozygous (Tt). To identify the unknown genotype of the plant it is crossed with a homozygous recessive plant.

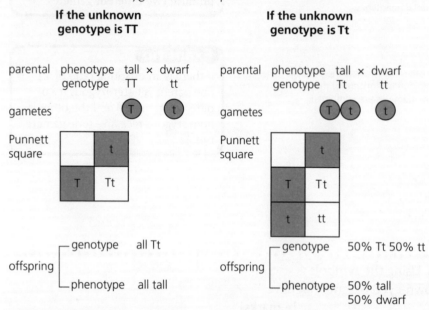

Exam tip

If both alleles from a parent are identical (homozygous) it is not necessary to use two identical gametes in the genetic cross – see Figure 10.5.

So if any dwarf plants are produced the unknown parent was heterozygous (Tt).

↑ **Figure 10.5 The test cross**

Sex determination in humans

Humans have 22 pairs of normal chromosomes and one pair of sex chromosomes. The male sex chromosomes are XY and females have two XX chromosomes. As the sex chromosomes (and alleles) act in the same way as in other genetic crosses, Figure 10.6 shows that equal numbers of boys and girls are produced.

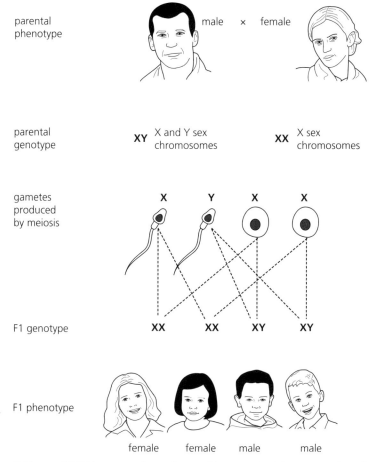

parental phenotype	male × female		
parental genotype	**XY** X and Y sex chromosomes	**XX** X sex chromosomes	
gametes produced by meiosis	X Y	X X	
F1 genotype	**XX** **XX**	**XY** **XY**	
F1 phenotype	female female	male male	

↑ **Figure 10.6 How equal numbers of boys and girls are produced**

As well as determining sex, sex chromosomes can carry genes and alleles that control other characteristics. As the Y chromosome does not contain any alleles, any recessive alleles carried on the X chromosome in males are not masked by a dominant partner and therefore show in the phenotype. In females where there are two X chromosomes the recessive condition can be masked by a dominant allele. Examples of sex-linked conditions are red-green colour blindness and haemophilia as shown in Figure 10.7.

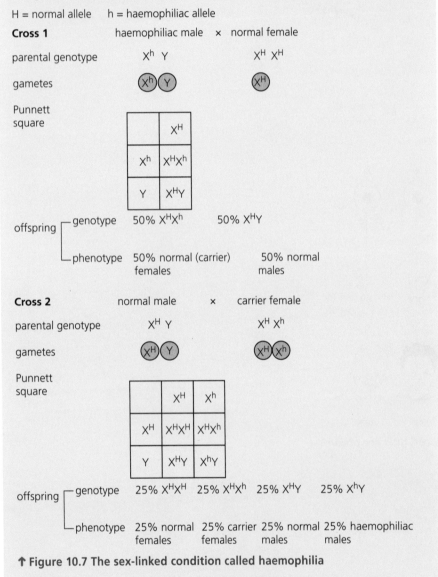

H = normal allele   h = haemophiliac allele

Cross 1   haemophiliac male × normal female

parental genotype X^h Y X^H X^H

gametes X^h Y X^H

Punnett
square

	X^H
X^h	$X^H X^h$
Y	$X^H Y$

offspring ┬ genotype   50% $X^H X^h$ 50% $X^H Y$

          └ phenotype   50% normal (carrier)   50% normal
                        females   males

Cross 2   normal male   ×   carrier female

parental genotype X^H Y X^H X^h

gametes X^H Y X^H X^h

Punnett
square

	X^H	X^h
X^H	$X^H X^H$	$X^H X^h$
Y	$X^H Y$	$X^h Y$

offspring ┬ genotype   25% $X^H X^H$ 25% $X^H X^h$ 25% $X^H Y$ 25% $X^h Y$

          └ phenotype   25% normal   25% carrier   25% normal   25% haemophiliac
                        females   females   males   males

↑ **Figure 10.7 The sex-linked condition called haemophilia**

These crosses show why haemophilia is usually found only in males. Very occasionally, females may inherit the condition.

1   Suggest two reasons why surgery may not be the best option for someone who has advanced pancreatic cancer.   **[2 marks]**

2   **a)** Explain the roles of mitosis and meiosis in maintaining constancy of chromosome number in a species.   **[3 marks]**

　　b) Explain the role of meiosis in providing variation.   **[2 marks]**

3   Flowers can be red or white in a certain type of flower. When two red flowers were crossed and their offspring counted the following results were obtained.

	Red flowers	**White flowers**
Number of offspring	143	57

　　a) i)   What genetic ratio do the offspring results approximate to?   **[1 mark]**

　　ii)   Explain why the offspring numbers do not fit the ratio exactly.   **[1 mark]**

　　b) Use a Punnett square to explain the outcome of this cross.   **[4 marks]**

4   Huntington's disease is a medical condition caused by the presence of a single allele. The following pedigree diagram shows the inheritance of Huntington's disease in a family through three generations.

Huntington's disease is caused by a non-sex-linked dominant allele.

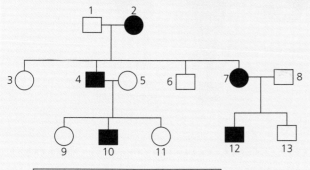

Key
☐ Normal male
○ Normal female
■ Male with Huntington's disease
● Female with Huntington's disease

　　a) How many male grandchildren do individuals 1 and 2 have?   **[1 mark]**

　　b) What is the evidence that the allele for Huntington's disease is dominant and not recessive?   **[1 mark]**

　　c) Explain the pattern of transmission of Huntington's disease between the grandparents (1 and 2) and their children.   **[3 marks]**

　　d) What is the probability that the next child of parents 7 and 8 will be a boy with Huntington's disease?   **[2 marks]**

Go online for the answers   Online

11 Reproduction, Fertility and Contraception

Sexual reproduction

Humans as with most animals, reproduce **sexually**. This involves the production of male and female gametes (sex cells) that combine to produce the next generation.

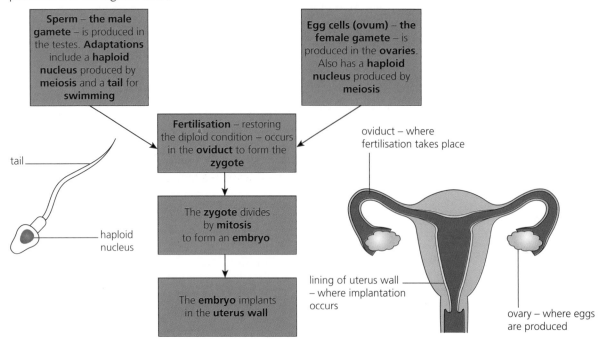

Sperm – the male gamete – is produced in the testes. **Adaptations** include a **haploid nucleus** produced by **meiosis** and a **tail** for **swimming**

Egg cells (ovum) – the female gamete – is produced in the **ovaries**. Also has a **haploid nucleus** produced by **meiosis**

Fertilisation – restoring the diploid condition – occurs in the **oviduct** to form the **zygote**

oviduct – where fertilisation takes place

tail

haploid nucleus

The **zygote** divides by **mitosis** to form an **embryo**

The **embryo** implants in the **uterus wall**

lining of uterus wall – where implantation occurs

ovary – where eggs are produced

Worked example

Explain the roles of meiosis and mitosis in fertilisation and the development of the human embryo. [3 marks]

Answer

Meiosis produces haploid gametes / gametes with half the number of chromosomes of other cells; ensures diploid number restored after fertilisation.

Mitosis maintains chromosome number / diploid number during growth of embryo.

Life in the uterus

Following implantation, the developing foetus differentiates as it grows to produce a variety of tissues and organs. As this happens it is supported by a number of structures.

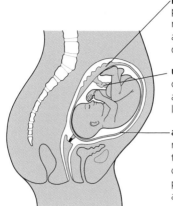

placenta
provides oxygen and nutrients to the foetus and removes carbon dioxide and urea

umbilical cord
carries the umbilical artery and the umbilical vein and links foetus to placenta

amnion
membrane that contains the amniotic fluid which cushions the foetus and protects it from knocks and bumps

↑ **Figure 11.1 The foetus in the uterus and the surrounding protective structures**

The placenta is adapted for diffusion by having a large surface area.

The placenta is subdivided into many villi (similar in shape to the villi in the intestine) that are in close contact with the uterine lining – these further increase the surface area contact between maternal and foetal blood systems.

Exam tip

Many of the adaptations of the placenta involve the creation of a large surface area for the diffusion of materials to and from the foetus.

Contraception (preventing pregnancy)

The table outlines the three main types of contraception.

Mechanical (condom)	**Chemical** (contraceptive pill)	**Surgical** (vasectomy or female sterilisation)
● A barrier preventing sperm from entering the female reproductive system	● Contains hormones that prevents eggs being released	● Cutting of sperm tubes or oviducts
● Easily obtained and can protect against sexually transmitted diseases (HIV, chlamydia and gonorrhoea)	● Very reliable ● Some side effects such as weight gain	● Prevents sperm being released and egg passing down oviduct respectively
● Unreliable if not used properly		● Virtually 100% reliable ● Very difficult to reverse

Exam tip

Questions often ask you to explain how specific types of contraception work.

Worked example

Explain how condoms prevent fertilisation.   [2 marks]

Answer

Condoms prevent the sperm from entering the female reproductive system, therefore sperm cannot fertilise the egg.

Sex hormones

Revised

1 **Testosterone** – produced by **testes** in **males**. Effects include:
   - sexual organs enlarge
   - body and pubic hair grows
   - voice deepens and body becomes more muscular
   - sexual awareness and drive increase.

2 **Oestrogen** – produced by **ovaries** in **females**. Effects include:
   - sexual organs and breasts enlarge
   - pubic hair grows
   - pelvis and hips widen
   - menstruation begins
   - sexual awareness and drive increases.

The human menstrual cycle

Revised

An approximately 28-day cycle in females in preparation for pregnancy:

- **menstruation** – blood-rich uterine lining breaks down if pregnancy does not occur during previous menstrual cycle

- **ovulation** – about 14 days into the cycle an egg is released – by this time the uterine lining has built up in preparation for pregnancy

- sexual intercourse can result in **pregnancy** if it occurs during a short window either side of ovulation.

Fertility problems and their treatment

Revised

Problems – many causes including **female** unable to produce eggs or blockages preventing movement of eggs down the oviducts and **males** having low sperm counts or impotence.

Treatments can involve:

1 giving females **fertility drugs** to increase egg production

2 collecting eggs from ovaries and adding to sperm in a test tube (*in-vitro* **fertilisation**, **IVF**)

3 **replacing embryos** formed back into the uterus.

Fertility treatments can raise **ethical issues** as IVF treatment can be used to screen for abnormalities or for particular characteristics, e.g. selecting the sex of the embryo.

1 Describe the main stages between fertilisation and implantation. [3 marks]

2 Describe and explain the key events of the menstrual cycle. [4 marks]

3 a) Suggest why females need to be given hormone treatment when having IVF treatment. [2 marks]

   b) Suggest two reasons why IVF is such an expensive procedure. [2 marks]

   c) Explain the term *in-vitro* fertilisation. [1 mark]

4 The following table shows the number of males of different ages having vasectomy operations in one hospital over a year long period in 2011.

Age range	Number of patients having a vasectomy
20–29	4
30–39	41
40–49	121
50–59	68
60+	10

   a) Describe the trend shown by the data in the table. [2 marks]

   b) Suggest reasons for the large difference between the data for the 20–29 and 40–49 age groups. [2 marks]

   c) Explain how a vasectomy prevents pregnancy. [2 marks]

5 a) Describe and explain the respective roles of the placenta and the umbilical cord in providing nourishment for the foetus. [4 marks]

   b) Describe the role of the amnion in protecting the foetus. [2 marks]

12 Applied Genetics

Mutations are changes in **chromosome number** or **structure**. Here are some examples of mutations that cause disease in humans.

- **Skin cancer** is caused by random changes to **gene structure**. The gene damage can be promoted by **UV light**.

- **Down syndrome** is caused by an error during meiosis. Sometimes the two chromosomes in a pair fail to segregate properly and one gamete ends up with 24 chromosomes. If this gamete is involved in fertilisation the Down syndrome child will have 47 chromosomes in each cell.

- **Haemophilia** is caused by a mutation producing a recessive allele in the blood clotting gene on an X chromosome.
  Cystic fibrosis is another inherited disease caused by a recessive allele.

Exam tip

Down syndrome is always caused by an extra chromosome in pair 21 – if you are asked to study a **karyograph** (complete set of chromosomes arranged in pairs) to identify if the individual has Down syndrome, check pair 21 (assuming they are numbered) to see if there are three rather than two chromosomes there.

Genetic screening   Revised ☐

Genetic screening can be used to identify the presence of genetic conditions in an individual, for example it can be used to test for the presence of Down syndrome and other conditions including cystic fibrosis in a foetus.

The current method for testing for Down syndrome is **amniocentesis**. This involves taking some foetal cells from the fluid in the amnion, growing these cells in the laboratory and checking how many chromosomes each cell has.

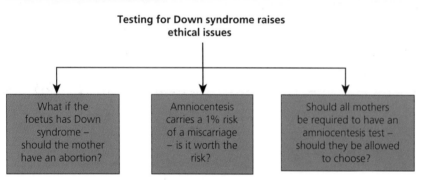

Testing for Down syndrome raises ethical issues

| What if the foetus has Down syndrome – should the mother have an abortion? | Amniocentesis carries a 1% risk of a miscarriage – is it worth the risk? | Should all mothers be required to have an amniocentesis test – should they be allowed to choose? |

Genetic screening advances raise many issues including:

- should screening be used for all genetic diseases?

- should we be allowed to screen for the sex of a child?

- should screening results be made available to insurance companies?

Worked example

Suggest two reasons why amniocentesis testing for Down syndrome is not compulsory for all mothers.   [2 marks]

Answer

Amniocentesis involves a risk of miscarriage – if all mothers were tested there would be many more miscarriages than Down syndrome babies detected; it would be expensive to test all mothers.

Genetic engineering

This involves adding a human gene to the DNA of another organism, e.g. bacteria – the other organism makes the product that the human DNA codes for.

Bacteria are genetically engineered to make human insulin (used in the treatment of diabetes).

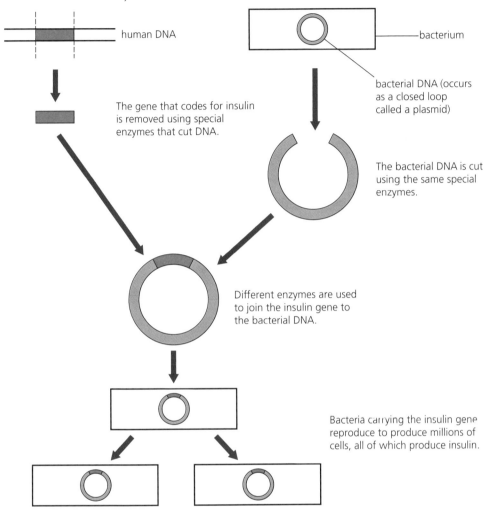

human DNA

bacterium

bacterial DNA (occurs as a closed loop called a plasmid)

The gene that codes for insulin is removed using special enzymes that cut DNA.

The bacterial DNA is cut using the same special enzymes.

Different enzymes are used to join the insulin gene to the bacterial DNA.

Bacteria carrying the insulin gene reproduce to produce millions of cells, all of which produce insulin.

The bacteria are grown in large fermenters that provide the best conditions for bacterial reproduction and allow easy extraction of insulin.

↑ Figure 12.1 Genetic engineering – making human insulin

Advantages of genetically engineered insulin:

● before genetic engineering the amount of insulin available was limited by the amount that could be extracted from dead animals in slaughterhouses. This restricted the amount that could be obtained and made the insulin relatively expensive.

● human insulin is slightly different in structure from the insulin of other animals – so insulin obtained from dead animals might not be as effective and can cause allergies.

Many other products are now made by genetic engineering.

> **Exam tip**
>
> In genetic engineering, enzymes are needed to both cut out the human insulin gene and also to cut a gap in the plasmid to allow the human gene to fit.

Cutting the human DNA

Special enzymes (**restriction enzymes**) cut the human gene in such a way as to leave overlapping strands of DNA. The same enzymes cut the bacterial plasmid (DNA) in the same way to leave complementary **sticky ends**. The sticky ends make it easy for the human and bacterial DNA to join through **base pairing**.

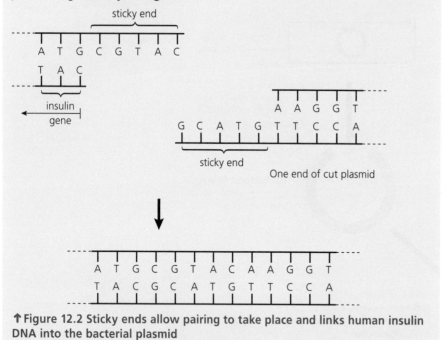

↑ Figure 12.2 Sticky ends allow pairing to take place and links human insulin DNA into the bacterial plasmid

Following the production of insulin it is **extracted**, **purified** and **packaged** in a process called **downstreaming**.

Revision Questions
Tested

1 Jill has a brother with cystic fibrosis and has just become pregnant for the first time. Give one argument for and one against genetically screening the foetus for the presence of cystic fibrosis. **[2 marks]**

2 a) Explain the advantage in using the same restriction enzyme to cut the bacterial plasmid and to cut out the human insulin gene in genetic engineering. **[2 marks]**

b) State and explain two advantages in using genetically engineered insulin in the treatment of diabetes. **[4 marks]**

3 a) Place the following structures into order of size starting with the smallest.

human gene : bacterium : plasmid **[1 mark]**

b) Describe and explain the process of adding a human gene into bacterial DNA during genetic engineering. **[3 marks]**

4 a) Copy the boxes below. Using lines, match the medical conditions below with their genetic causes.

medical condition	genetic cause
Cystic fibrosis	Chromosome mutation
Down syndrome	Inherited disease
Skin cancer	Gene mutation

[2 marks]

Go online for the answers

Online

74 12 Applied Genetics

13 Variation and Selection

Variation

Living organisms that belong to the same species resemble each other but usually differ from each other in a number of ways. These differences are called **variation**.

Variation for a particular feature is usually a mixture of genetic and environmental factors. For example, a person can only grow to their full height as determined by their genes if they have been healthy and have a good diet during their childhood.

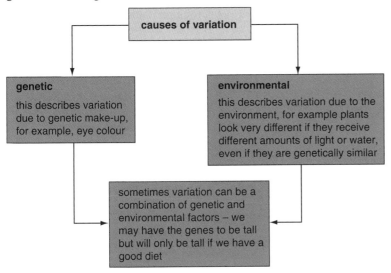

↑ **Figure 13.1 Causes of variation**

Variation can be **continuous** or **discontinuous** as shown in the table.

Variation	Explanation	Examples	Graphical representation
Continuous	Gradual change in a characteristic across a population with no distinct categories; most individuals will be around the mode / mean with fewer people at either extreme	Height / mass in humans	Histogram
Discontinuous	Individuals can be grouped into distinct groups with no overlap	Tongue rolling, ABO blood groups	Bar chart

Exam tip

When drawing bar charts to show discontinuous variation there should be gaps between the bars.

Natural selection and Charles Darwin

Darwin was the first person to understand the significance of **natural selection**.

Natural selection can be summarised as:

- **variation** exists between individuals in a population
- if there is competition for resources there will be a **struggle for existence**
- the best adapted survive – **survival of the fittest**
- the best adapted survive to **breed** and pass their **genes** (characteristics) on to their **offspring**.

Antibiotic resistance

Antibiotic resistance in bacteria is an example of natural selection in action.

- When treated with an antibiotic some bacteria may already be resistant (due to a **mutation**).
- These bacteria survive as the rest are killed.
- The resistant bacteria survive to breed and soon become the dominant type in the population.

Exam tip

Normally the numbers of antibiotic resistant (mutated) bacteria in a bacterial population are very low as they have no advantage when there is no antibiotic present – they only have an advantage when an antibiotic is added.

Exam tip

The antibiotic resistant bacteria are already present in the bacterial population when the antibiotic is added – the antibiotic does not cause the mutation.

Worked example

In a typical pasture there may be a few plants that have a gene resistant to high levels of copper in the soil. In these conditions the normal grasses grow better than the copper-resistant variety. However, in areas where the soil is contaminated with copper the copper-resistant variety may make up over 90% of the plants present. Explain this observation. [4 marks]

Answer

The following four points for 4 marks.

- In copper-contaminated areas the resistant gene is an advantage.
- Copper-resistant plants are more likely to survive / are fitter / better adapted.
- Copper-resistant plants are more likely to have offspring / pass genes on to next generation.
- Percentage of copper-resistant genes increases over time in the population.

The link between natural selection and evolution

Revised

Natural selection can explain how **species** have **changed gradually** over a very long time in a process called **evolution**.

Over a very long period of time a **species** changes as certain characteristics in individuals are favoured (and more likely to be passed on to offspring) – eventually the species may be very different to how it started out.

Evolution is a **continuing process** as all species are subject to natural selection and therefore change.

Extinction

Revised

Sometimes entire species may not be well enough adapted to survive in a changing world and can no longer survive – they may become **extinct**, e.g. mammoths and dinosaurs are species that have been extinct for some time.

Many organisms are **endangered** (at risk of extinction) due to climate change, hunting by man, habitat destruction and many other reasons. Currently both mountain gorillas and pandas are examples of endangered species.

Revision Questions

Tested

1 Over time many species of predators and their prey have become more agile and able to run faster.

  Use your understanding of natural selection to explain this phenomenon. **[3 marks]**

2 The peppered moth exists in two forms: light coloured and black. In non-polluted areas the light form is well camouflaged on the bark of trees whereas the black form is easily spotted and eaten by birds. In these areas the light forms are more common.

  In industrial areas where the trees are heavily polluted with soot the black forms are more common. Explain why. **[2 marks]**

3 Compare and contrast the terms 'natural selection' and 'evolution'. **[2 marks]**

Go online for the answers

Online

14 The Circulatory System

The circulatory system has two main functions:

● **transport** – blood cells, food (glucose / amino acids), carbon dioxide, urea

● **protection** against disease.

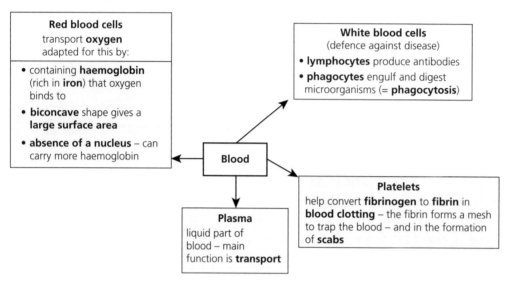

Red blood cells
transport **oxygen**
adapted for this by:

• containing **haemoglobin** (rich in **iron**) that oxygen binds to

• **biconcave** shape gives a **large surface area**

• **absence of a nucleus** – can carry more haemoglobin

White blood cells
(defence against disease)

• **lymphocytes** produce antibodies

• **phagocytes** engulf and digest microorganisms (= **phagocytosis**)

Blood

Platelets
help convert **fibrinogen** to **fibrin** in **blood clotting** – the fibrin forms a mesh to trap the blood – and in the formation of **scabs**

Plasma
liquid part of blood – main function is **transport**

↑ Figure 14.1 Main components of blood

The blood vessels

Revised

Vessel	Blood flow	Vessel wall	Blood Pressure	Valves
Artery	Away from heart	Thick – contains **muscle** for strength and **elastic fibres** to allow expansion as blood pulses through – moderating the blood flow	High	None
Vein	Back to heart	Thinner than artery – some muscle and few or no elastic fibres	Low	Yes
Capillary	Joins arteries and veins	One-cell thick	Low	None

> **Exam tip**
>
> Make sure you know how each type of blood vessel is adapted for its function.

The circulatory system

The circulatory system includes the heart and blood vessels involved in pumping and transporting blood throughout the body. Figure 14.1 shows the main parts of the circulatory system.

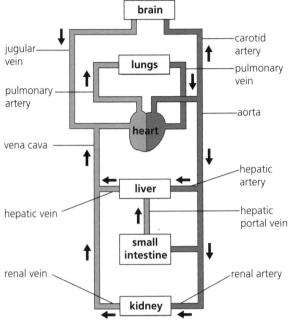

Note: Only students taking GCSE Biology (Higher Tier) need to know the carotid artery and jugular vein.

↑ Figure 14.2 The circulatory system

The heart

The heart is the organ that pumps blood round the body. Figure 14.3 shows that the body has a **double circulation** – the blood travels through the heart twice for each complete circuit of the body.

pulmonary artery – carries deoxygenated blood to lungs

aorta – carries oxygenated blood at high pressure around body

pulmonary vein – returns oxygenated blood from lungs

right atrium – receives blood from body

left atrium – receives blood from lungs

valves – prevent backflow of blood

vena cava – returns blood from body

right ventricle – pumps blood to lungs

left ventricle – pumps blood around body

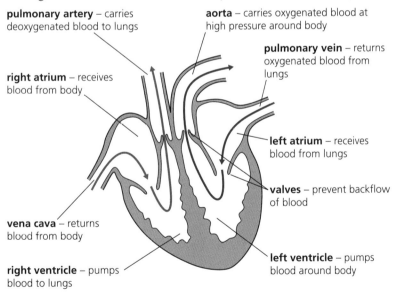

↑ Figure 14.3 The heart

- The ventricles are thicker than the atria as they are the chambers that pump the blood.
- The left ventricle has a thicker muscular wall than the right ventricle as it pumps blood round the body – not just to the lungs.
- The valves prevent backflow and make sure that the heart acts as a unidirectional pump.

Heart disease

Heart disease is caused by the arteries becoming clogged up with fatty substances.

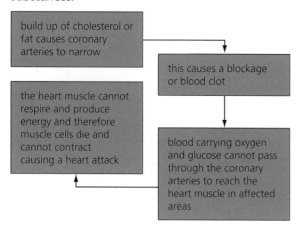

↑ Figure 14.4 Heart disease

> **Exam tip**
>
> The term **coronary heart disease** (**CHD**) is often used as it is the **coronary arteries** that are affected in a heart attack because:
> - they are the arteries that supply the heart with blood
> - they are very thin so become blocked more easily than many other arteries.

Strokes

Strokes are caused by circulatory blockages in the **brain** – as it is a different organ to the heart the blockage and death of brain cells have different effects – as a part of the brain may stop functioning properly, paralysis in a part of the body may result.

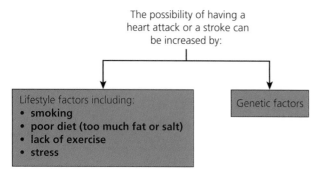

Worked example 1

Explain how a heart attack occurs.   [3 marks]

Answer

Three of the following points for 3 marks:
- coronary arteries
- become blocked with cholesterol / fat
- this stops glucose / oxygen reaching the heart muscle
- no respiration / energy produced
- heart muscle no longer contracts.

Other circulatory diseases

Some circulatory diseases are caused by a shortage of specific blood components.

An example is anaemia.

- Anaemia is caused by a shortage of red blood cells.
- Usually due to not enough iron in the diet or blood loss.

Worked example 2

Suggest why people with anaemia often lack energy. [3 marks]

Answer

- shortage of haemoglobin / red blood cells
- less oxygen can be transported
- less respiration for energy.

Exercise and the circulatory system

Revised ☐

Regular exercise benefits the circulatory system by:

- burning up fat
- preventing obesity
- strengthening the heart muscle – a stronger heart pumps more blood per beat – therefore has to beat less often.

> **Exam tip**
>
> Questions on exercise often involve graphs showing the effect of exercise on pulse rate.

Blood donation

Revised ☐

Donated blood is used in giving **transfusions** for many reasons including:

- a patient has lost a lot of blood in an accident or during surgery
- sometimes patients need particular blood components, e.g. platelets or other clotting agents because their blood does not clot properly.

In Northern Ireland (as elsewhere) there is often a shortage of blood donors.

There are many reasons:

- many people do not become donors (over 90% of the population)
- only 'healthy' people can give blood
- there is increasing demand for blood
- donated blood can only be stored for a short period of time
- usually only people aged between 17–70 can donate blood
- some religious groups do not believe in donating blood (or receiving transfusions).

Plasma, tissue fluid and lymph

The flow diagram shows the relationship between plasma, tissue fluid and lymph.

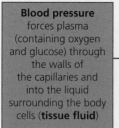

| **Blood pressure** forces plasma (containing oxygen and glucose) through the walls of the capillaries and into the liquid surrounding the body cells (**tissue fluid**) | → | The oxygen and glucose diffuse into the body cells and are replaced by carbon dioxide diffusing out. Much of this liquid containing carbon dioxide **re-enters the capillaries** by **osmosis** | → | Some liquid does not re-enter the capillaries but is 'mopped up' by **lymph vessels**. The fluid in the lymph vessels (**lymph**) eventually drains back into the circulatory system |

Revision Questions

1 a) i)   State three differences between arteries and veins.   **[3 marks]**

   ii)   Explain the reason for one structural difference between arteries and veins. **[1 marks]**

   b) Explain what is meant by the term 'double circulatory
   system'.   **[2 marks]**

2 a) The following diagram represents part of the circulatory system.

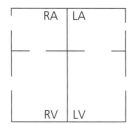

Key
RA = right atrium
LA = left atrium
RV = right ventricle
LV = left ventricle

Copy and complete the diagram by drawing four blood vessels to show the circulation of blood from:

   ● the heart to the body organs

   ● the body organs to the heart

   ● the heart to the lungs

   ● the lungs to the heart.   **[1 mark]**

b) Use arrows to show the direction of blood flow in each vessel. [1 mark]

c) On your diagram label the pulmonary vein. [1 mark]

d) Describe one way in which the pulmonary artery differs from all other arteries in the body. [1 mark]

3 Carrie is an athlete who trains hard. Her resting pulse rate is measured as 68 beats per minute (bpm) and during a 20 minute run it climbs steadily to reach a plateau of 95 bpm 5 minutes into the exercise. Immediately after stopping the run Carrie's pulse rate begins to slow down at a steady rate until it reaches her resting value 7 minutes after the exercise.

a) Using the information provided, draw a graph of Carrie's pulse rate from 5 minutes before she started the run until 10 minutes after she stopped running. [4 marks]

b) Use the information to calculate Carrie's recovery time. [1 mark]

c) Carrie's resting pulse rate is lower than that of her friend Katie, who seldom exercises.

    i) Explain why Carrie has a lower resting pulse rate. [2 marks]

    ii) Carrie and Katie both have to run to catch the bus. Suggest two differences between the effects this will have on each of their pulse rates. [2 marks]

4 Tissue fluid is the liquid that bathes body cells.

a) Explain the respective roles of blood pressure and capillary structure in the formation of tissue fluid. [2 marks]

b) Suggest two functions of tissue fluid. [2 marks]

c) Explain the formation of lymph. [2 marks]

Go online for the answers   Online

15 Microorganisms, Defence against Disease, Medicines and Drugs

The theory of spontaneous generation

Revised

Before Pasteur's famous experiment in 1861 most people assumed that microorganisms spontaneously appeared from non-living material. Pasteur was able to disprove the theory of spontaneous generation by showing that microbes could only contaminate liquids and foods if they were already present or could gain access to the samples. He used specially designed 'swan-neck' flasks in his experiment as shown in Figure 15.1.

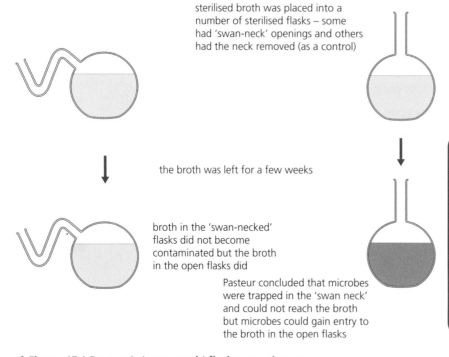

sterilised broth was placed into a number of sterilised flasks – some had 'swan-neck' openings and others had the neck removed (as a control)

the broth was left for a few weeks

broth in the 'swan-necked' flasks did not become contaminated but the broth in the open flasks did

Pasteur concluded that microbes were trapped in the 'swan neck' and could not reach the broth but microbes could gain entry to the broth in the open flasks

> **Exam tip**
>
> It is important that you understand the need for **controlled variables** in experiments / investigations such as Pasteur's. Examples include:
> - the type of broth used must be the same in each flask
> - the flasks must be kept at the same temperature
> - the flasks must be left for the same length of time.

↑ **Figure 15.1 Pasteur's 'swan-neck' flasks experiment**

Pasteurisation is a technique used to reduce contamination of milk and other products.

1 The milk is heated to a **high temperature** – but **below boiling point** as boiling affects flavour.

2 It is then **rapidly chilled** to a low temperature.

3 Pasteurisation kills most bacteria present.

Disease-causing microorganisms

Revised ☐

Many microorganisms are harmful and can cause disease.

The table gives examples of the main types of disease-causing microorganisms and how they are spread, prevented and treated.

Microbe	Type	Spread	Control / prevention / treatment
HIV which leads to AIDS	Virus	Exchange of body fluids during sex, infected blood	Using a condom reduces risk of infection, as does drug addicts not sharing needles No cure
Rubella	Virus	Airborne (droplet infection) through coughing and sneezing	Prevented by MMR vaccination
Measles	Virus	Airborne (droplet infection) or by contact	Prevented by MMR vaccination
Mumps	Virus	Airborne (droplet infection)	Prevented by MMR vaccination
Colds and flu	Virus	Airborne (droplet infection)	Flu vaccination for targeted groups
Polio	Virus	Usually spread through drinking water contaminated with faeces	The polio vaccination has currently eradicated polio in the UK
Salmonella food poisoning	Bacterium	From contaminated food	Always cooking food thoroughly and not mixing cooked and uncooked foods can control spread, treatment by antibiotics
Gonorrhoea	Bacterium	Sexual contact	Using a condom reduces risk of infection, treatment by antibiotics
Tuberculosis	Bacterium	Airborne (droplet infection)	BCG vaccination, if contracted, treated with drugs including antibiotics
Chlamydia	Bacterium	Sexual contact	Using a condom reduces risk of infection, treatment by antibiotics
Athlete's foot	Fungus	Contact	Reduce infection risk by avoiding direct contact in areas where spores are likely to be present, e.g. wear 'flip flops' in changing rooms / swimming pools

Defence against disease

Revised ☐

Initial defence involves stopping microorganisms gaining entry.

Skin	Barrier to microbes gaining entry
Mucous membranes	Thin membranes in nose and respiratory system that trap and expel microorganisms – the microorganisms are trapped in the mucous lining of the membrane
Clotting	Closes wounds quickly to prevent microorganisms gaining entry (and also preventing the loss of blood)

The role of white blood cells in defence

If microorganisms do gain entry to the body it is the role of the white blood cells to combat infection.

Lymphocytes

These white blood cells **produce antibodies** when a microorganism enters the blood.

- Microorganisms have special chemical markers called **antigens**
- The antigens on the microorganism stimulate the lymphocytes to produce **antibodies**
- The antibodies are **complementary in shape** to the antigens and latch on the antigens linking the microorganisms together
- This **immobilises** (clumps) the microorganisms and they can then be destroyed by **phagocytes**

Phagocytes

These white blood cells surround microorganisms and **engulf** (eat) them.

- Once taken in, enzymes **digest** and destroy the microorganisms

> **Exam tip**
>
> As each type of microorganism has different types (and shapes) of antigen, each type of antibody has a unique shape complementary to the microorganism it responds to – this is why we have different types of antibody for each disease-causing microorganism.

Immunity

If a person cannot get a particular disease they are **immune**. Immunity is caused when the body has enough antibodies (or can produce them quickly enough) to combat infection. Figure 15.2 summarises the types of immunity and describes how they develop.

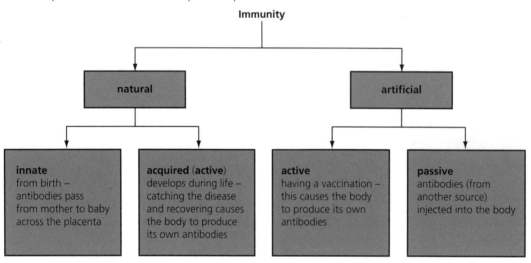

↑ **Figure 15.2 Immunity**

The graph in Figure 15.3 shows how antibody levels in the body change following infection – an example of acquired (active) natural immunity.

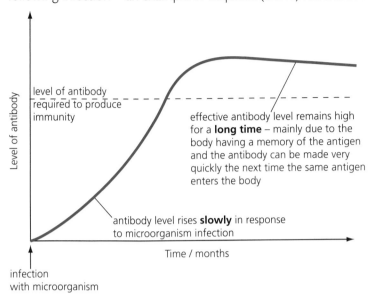

↑ Figure 15.3 Active immunity (acquired by having had the disease)

The graph in Figure 15.4 shows how antibody levels change following vaccination. This is artificial active immunity.

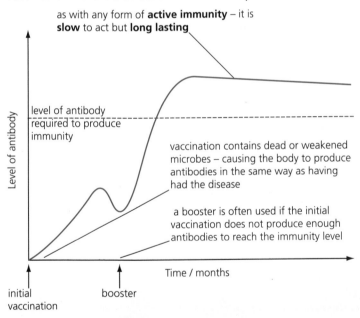

↑ Figure 15.4 Active immunity (by vaccination)

The long acting response shown in Figures 15.3 and 15.4 (active immunity) is due to the initial infection / vaccination causing the production of **memory lymphocyte cells** – these remain in the body and can rapidly produce antibodies again if re-infection occurs (**the secondary response**).

The graph in Figure 15.5 shows how antibody levels change following an injection of ready-made antibodies – passive immunity.

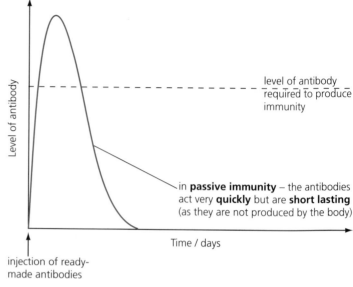

level of antibody required to produce immunity

in **passive immunity** – the antibodies act very **quickly** but are **short lasting** (as they are not produced by the body)

Level of antibody

Time / days

injection of ready-made antibodies

↑ Figure 15.5 Passive immunity (by injection of ready-made antibodies)

Worked example 1

a) State one similarity and one difference between active and passive immunity. [2 marks]

b) Describe and explain one advantage of each type of immunity. [4 marks]

Answers

a) Similarity: provide immunity through antibodies; difference: in active immunity antibodies are produced by the body and in passive immunity they are injected into the body.

b) Passive immunity: fast; as antibodies are ready-made and can act immediately; active immunity: is long lasting; as the body has been programmed to make the antibodies and can make them if the same microbes enter the body again.

More about vaccinations

Revised

Jenner and the first vaccination

Jenner noticed that milkmaids who caught the minor illness cowpox did not catch smallpox. He concluded that having had the cowpox gave them protection. To test this he deliberately infected a young boy in 1796 (James Phipps) with cowpox and then deliberately infected him sometime later with smallpox. The boy did not catch smallpox. The cowpox was very similar to smallpox and immunity had built up to both diseases in the boy. This was the first vaccination.

Travel and vaccinations

● People who travel to some foreign countries need **special vaccinations** – vaccinations that are not routinely given to people in Britain.

● This is to provide **antibodies** (protection) against microorganisms (**antigens**) that they have previously not encountered.

Antibiotics

Antibiotics are chemicals, e.g. penicillin, that kill **bacteria** or reduce their growth – they are used to combat diseases causes by bacteria.

Some bacteria can develop **resistance** to antibiotics (see Chapter 13) – the overuse of antibiotics is largely responsible. Some bacteria are resistant to many types of antibiotics – these are often called '**superbugs**' – MRSA is a well known example.

It is difficult to eradicate / prevent the spread of 'superbugs' in hospitals for a number of reasons:

- antibiotics have no effect
- hospitals are an 'antibiotic rich' environment, therefore encouraging the development of resistance
- there are many patients with open wounds and weakened immune systems.

Measures are being taken to reduce the incidence of 'superbugs' including:

- further increasing hygiene levels
- greater control of antibiotic use
- isolation of patients with 'superbug' infections.

> **Exam tip**
>
> **Mutations** make bacteria antibiotic resistant. Antibiotic-resistant bacteria are resistant before an antibiotic is used – the antibiotic does *not* cause antibiotic resistance.

> **Exam tip**
>
> Antibiotics only work against **bacterial** infections; they have no effect against viral infections, such as colds and flu.

Working with microbes in the laboratory – the use of aseptic techniques

When working with microbes in a school environment there are important health and safety precautions that need to be followed when growing or culturing microbes. These include:

- not eating or drinking in the laboratory
- culturing microbes in sealed containers
- not culturing microbes at body temperature
- using sterile loops for transferring cultures
- flaming the necks of culture bottles to prevent contamination
- sterilising or disposing of all equipment after use
- washing hands thoroughly at the end of the work.

It is very important that the microbes you are working with do not contaminate anything else and the safety measures described above will help prevent this. It is also important that the microbes themselves are not contaminated from other microbes in the air or on surrounding surfaces. The use of **aseptic techniques**, listed above, in the laboratory helps to prevent contamination.

A typical laboratory experiment involves investigating the effect of a range of antibiotics on bacteria as shown in Figure 15.6.

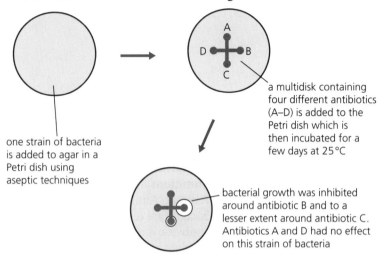

one strain of bacteria is added to agar in a Petri dish using aseptic techniques

a multidisk containing four different antibiotics (A–D) is added to the Petri dish which is then incubated for a few days at 25°C

bacterial growth was inhibited around antibiotic B and to a lesser extent around antibiotic C. Antibiotics A and D had no effect on this strain of bacteria

↑ **Figure 15.6 Investigating the effect of antibiotics on bacteria**

Discovering medicines   Revised

The discovery of penicillin

1 Alexander Fleming was growing bacteria in agar plates when he noticed that one of his plates was infected with fungi.

2 He noticed that around the fungus no bacteria were growing – conclusion: something was diffusing from the fungus that killed the bacteria.

3 He was unable to isolate the chemical responsible but some years later two other scientists (Florey and Chain) were able to isolate the chemical responsible.

4 The chemical was penicillin – it went on to become the first commercially produced antibiotic.

Making penicillin commercially

The fungi that produces penicillin are grown in large **fermenters** (biodigesters) that create the perfect conditions for fungal growth. **Downstreaming** (extraction, purification and packaging) of penicillin completes the process.

Worked example 2

Explain three ways that fermenters can maximise penicillin production.

[3 marks]

Answer

Any three of the following:

● optimum temperature for enzyme activity

● optimum oxygen levels for respiration

● waste products removed to avoid contamination

● nutrients added to prevent food source becoming limiting.

Alcohol

The diagram below identifies some of the reasons why some people drink too much alcohol, summarises the harm it can do, and outlines strategies for reducing the harm caused by alcohol.

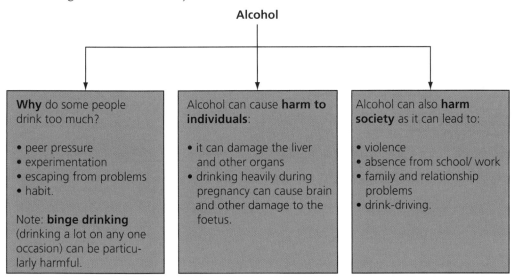

Alcohol

Why do some people drink too much?

- peer pressure
- experimentation
- escaping from problems
- habit.

Note: **binge drinking** (drinking a lot on any one occasion) can be particularly harmful.

Alcohol can cause **harm to individuals**:

- it can damage the liver and other organs
- drinking heavily during pregnancy can cause brain and other damage to the foetus.

Alcohol can also **harm society** as it can lead to:

- violence
- absence from school/ work
- family and relationship problems
- drink-driving.

There are many ways to **reduce the harm** caused by alcohol:

- drink less on each occasion, e.g. try low-alcohol drinks
- drink on fewer occasions, e.g. not during the week
- education – understand about units and the problems alcohol can cause
- never drink and drive
- do not drink alcohol until the legal age limit.

Smoking

Smoking can seriously damage health as summarised in the table.

Substance in cigarette smoke	Harmful effect(s)
Tar	Causes **bronchitis** (narrowing of the bronchi and bronchioles), **emphysema** (damage to alveoli that reduces the surface area for gas exchange) and **lung cancer** (caused by abnormal cell division in lung cells)
Nicotine	**Addictive** and affects **heart rate**
Carbon monoxide	Combines with red blood cells to reduce the **oxygen-carrying capacity** of the blood

Illegal drugs

Cannabis and cocaine are two of the most common illegal drugs.

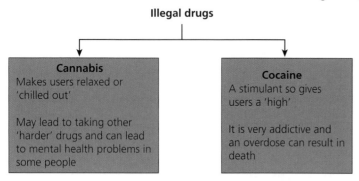

Illegal drugs

Cannabis
Makes users relaxed or 'chilled out'

May lead to taking other 'harder' drugs and can lead to mental health problems in some people

Cocaine
A stimulant so gives users a 'high'

It is very addictive and an overdose can result in death

Increasing (or even conflicting) scientific evidence about the use and misuse of drugs (both legal and illegal) has contributed to relatively recent changes in the following areas:

● the legal position of cannabis

● changes to alcohol licensing arrangements

● smoking bans in public places.

Revision Questions
Tested

1 Mary went to the doctor as she had a sore throat caused by a bacterial infection. Her sister Joanna was not feeling well either; the doctor diagnosed that Joanna was suffering from mumps.

 Explain why the doctor gave Mary an antibiotic but did not give Joanna an antibiotic. **[3 marks]**

2 Explain what is meant by the antibody-antigen reaction. **[3 marks]**

3 Jack and Jill were exposed to the rubella virus. Jill, but not Jack, had previously been given the MMR vaccination, which includes a vaccination against rubella.

 Describe and explain the difference in their immune responses. **[4 marks]**

4 Describe how you would use aseptic technique to transfer bacteria from one Petri dish that contains bacteria to another sterile Petri dish without contamination. **[5 marks]**

5 Patrick would like to give up smoking but finds it very hard to stop.

 a) Name the chemical in cigarette smoke that makes it difficult for Patrick to stop. **[1 mark]**

 b) Patrick's father Ollie has smoked for many years and he is always short of energy to the extent that he can barely climb a set of stairs. Explain how the tar and carbon monoxide in cigarette smoke have contributed to Ollie's lack of energy. **[5 marks]**

Go online for the answers
Online

Index

H

habitat 40

haemophilia 66, 72

haploid number 59, 68

heart 79–80

heart disease 80

heterozygosity 61–5

homozygosity 61–5

hormones

    human 33, 36–7, 70

    plant 38

humus 44

I

immunity 86–8

indicator species 49

insulin 37, 73–4

L

leaves 10, 11–13, 31, 54

light

    in the eye 34

    photosynthesis and 11, 12, 13, 14, 15

    plant response to 38

limiting factors 15–16

lungs 27–9, 31

lymph 82

lymphocytes 86

M

magnification 8

meiosis 59, 60, 65, 68

menstrual cycle 70

meristems 9

microorganisms

    disease and 85

    in the laboratory 89–90

minerals 14, 19, 47–8

mitosis 59, 60, 68

mutations 72, 76, 89

N

natural selection 76–7

negative feedback 37

nervous system 33, 35–6

neurones 33, 35, 36

nitrogen cycle 46

nutrient cycles 44–6

O

oestrogen 70

organisms

    classification 41–2

    organisation 9

osmosis 51–2

ovulation 70

oxygen

    from photosynthesis 11, 12–13, 14

    in respiration 14, 31

P

passive immunity 86, 88

pasteurisation 84

peer review 58

penicillin 90

phagocytes 86

phenotypes 62, 64

photosynthesis 11–16, 45

phototropism 38

plant cells 7, 9, 47, 52

plants 41

    hormones in 38

    osmosis 52

    transpiration 52, 53–4

    see also leaves; photosynthesis

plasma 78, 82

platelets 78

population 40, 42

protein 18, 57

Punnett squares 62, 63, 64

pyramids of biomass 43

pyramids of numbers 43

R

receptors 33, 36

recessive alleles 62, 66, 72

red blood cells 78, 81

reflex actions 36

reproduction

    asexual 60

    sexual 68–9

respiration 31

    aerobic 31, 32

    anaerobic 32

    photosynthesis and 14

respiratory system 27, 29–30, 31

root hair cells 47

S

sampling 40–1

sex chromosomes 65–6

sex-linked conditions 66, 72

sexual reproduction 68–9

smoking 91

spontaneous generation 84

starch 11–12, 14

stem cells 9

strokes 80

'superbugs' 89

synapses 35

T

test cross 64

testosterone 70

tissue fluid 82

transpiration 52, 53–4

U

uterus 68, 69

V

vaccinations 86, 87, 88

variation 59, 75, 76

veins 78

villi 21, 22

viruses 41

vitamins 18, 19

voluntary actions 36

W

water

    in the body 19

    osmosis 51–2

    in plants 52, 53–4

white blood cells 78, 86